Cheesemaking and Dairying

Katie Thear

Broad Leys Publishing Ltd

Cheesemaking and Dairying

First published: The Home Dairying Book. Broad Leys Publishing. 1978.
Second edition: Home Dairying. Batsford. 1983.
Third edition: Home and Farm Dairying. Broad Leys Publishing. 1988.

New revised edition first published 2003 by Broad Leys Publishing Ltd.

A catalogue record for this book is available from the British Library.

ISBN 0 906137 33 0

Cover photographs: Katie Thear

Outside front cover: A range of cheeses in the author's garden.

Outside back cover:
Top photograph - Monkland Cheese Dairy, Hereford
Centre and bottom photographs - The author's cheesemaking in progress

This book is dedicated to the memory of my mother
who taught me what she knew.

For details of other publications please contact the publishers:
Broad Leys Publishing Ltd
1 Tenterfields,
Newport, Saffron Walden,
Essex CB11 3UW, UK.
Tel/Fax: 01799 541065
E-mail: kdthear@btinternet.com
Website: www.kdthear.btinternet.co.uk

Contents

Preface

Cheesemaking is an art as well as a science. A good cheese is the product of heart as well as mind, but relying on one to the exclusion of the other may lead to disaster. *'A judicious blend of both is more perfect than either'* it is said, so I have tried to blend traditional wisdom and experience with modern scientific knowledge in this book.

My mother learnt to make Welsh farmhouse cheese in the traditional way, early in the last century, and her experience was a major influence when I subsequently came to cheesemaking. To her tuition I added scientific and technical expertise by attending various cheesemaking and dairying courses, and subsequently made cheeses and other products on a regular basis from the milk of our cow and goats.

This book first saw publication as *The Home Dairying Book* in 1978. It proved an immediate success, becoming known as 'the little red dairy book' on account of its cover; it was reprinted twice in that format. I have been touched by the number of people (many of whom now make cheeses commercially) who tell me that it was their introduction to the world of cheesemaking.

In 1983, a great deal of new material was included and my original book was published as *Home Dairying* by Batsford. In 1988, following several visits to French, Dutch and American dairy farms, a new edition called *Home and Farm Dairying* was published, taking into account the increasing number of smallholders who were then making cheeses and other dairy products.

Now, with the advent of a new generation of cheesemakers, and following further visits to dairies in Britain and Europe, the time has come to publish a new and updated edition of an old favourite. My thanks are due to all the organisations, dairies and individual cheesemakers who have helped by contributing recipes, advice, information and in some cases, photographs.

Katie Thear, Newport, 2003

The first edition published in 1978

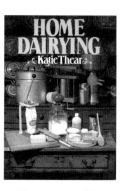

The second edition published in 1983.

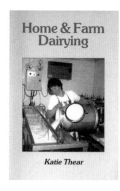

The third edition published in 1988.

Introduction

Blessed are the cheesemakers. (Life of Brian)

Cheesemaking is an ancient art. No-one is certain where it originated, but there is evidence to suggest that it was made in Macedonia, the Egypt of the Pharoahs and in many parts of Asia before it ever appeared in Europe. Wherever it came from there would be few who would disagree with the ancient Greeks that it is 'a gift from the gods'.

This book covers the whole aspect of home dairying although, as with earlier editions, its prime coverage is making cheese. There is also practical information on producing cream, making butter, ice cream and yoghurt.

It is applicable to those who are experimenting in their own kitchens as well as to those who are producing cheese or other products for sale. It is surprising how many started producing cheeses for the home and then went on to setting up a small, commercial enterprise.

It is possible to produce versions of most cheeses, although there will be obvious variations. Some traditional cheeses were made not only from the milk of specific dairy animals but also from specific breeds, and from milk produced at different times of the year. The area of the country, the type of pasture and other environmental conditions also played a part.

Some names are copyrighted to those who have a patent for them, or to specific areas. Where such cheeses are referred to in this book, they should be regarded as 'types' rather than the originals. For example, Stilton and Gorgonzola should be regarded as Stilton-type and Gorgonzola-type. Those who make a cheese for sale are advised to give it their own specific name.

Anyone who is considering making cheeses for sale would also be well advised to join *The Specialist Cheesemakers' Association.* Formed relatively recently, it is an excellent source of help and advice for its members. There are also many useful courses available on cheesemaking and dairying. In recent years, some excellent new cheeses and other dairy products have found their way into supermarkets and delicatessens all over Britain.

There is, of course, a considerable amount of legislation that needs to be followed by commercial producers. Further details of the cheese and dairying regulations are to be found in Appendix I.

Finally, we come back to the home producer who is just as capable of producing a fine cheese in the kitchen as in the grandest dairy. It should not be forgotten that the first Stilton was made by a Mrs Parlett, the sister of the local innkeeper in the village of Stilton in Cambridgeshire. She probably never thought that it was destined to become one of the great cheeses of the world.

The author's kitchen with equipment for making hard and soft cheeses, ice cream, butter and yoghurt.

A small cheese dairy where curd is in the process of being skimmed from the whey in the cheese vat. The staff wear overalls and head coverings to meet hygiene regulations.

The Dairy

Good huswife in dairie that needs not be tolde,
Deserveth hir fee to be paid hir in golde.

(Thomas Tusser, 16th Century)

Most country houses and many cottages had dairies or a buttery room in the past. My old home in Wales had a buttery where milk from our cows was left to set and ripen before being churned into butter in an 'end-over-end- churn. Here, too, were cheeses in various stages of production, while the buttermilk left over from churning provided cool drinks of *llaeth enwyn* or buttermilk.

Those making cheeses or other products for home consumption will be using their kitchens and pantries for dairying operations, and of course, there are no regulations that apply in this case. The situation is different for those who wish to sell their products. The premises must be registered and are subject to inspection by Environmental Health inspectors. There are regulations in relation to food safety, weights and measures, labelling and descriptions, and so on. They are listed in Appendix I.

Environment

Whatever the scale, cleanliness of the environment, equipment, milk and milk handlers is vital. After use, everything should be rinsed in cold water rather than hot, otherwise the deposits will harden on the surface. They are then washed in hot water and detergent and finally rinsed in hot water. For commercial premises, dairy detergents and hypochlorites are available. Final rinsing is vital because any anti-bacterial cleaner on the surface can inhibit growth of the necessary bacteria.

Working surfaces should be cleaned in a similar way. Avoid having anything to do with bread making or fruit preserving left lying around. The yeasts associated with these activities can adversely affect cheese and yoghurt.

A commercial dairy will vary depending on its activities. It may simply be for processing and packaging milk after milking, or it could be for making yoghurt for sale. It may be a more elaborate environment for making cheeses.

Three separate areas are required to cater for the different stages of cheesemaking. These are for *production*, *drying* and then *ripening* or *maturing*. (Ripening usually refers to soft cheeses, while maturing refers to pressed cheeses). In an average kitchen, this will probably mean the kitchen itself for production, with a pantry or utility room for the second two stages. A temperature of 21-24°C is the ideal environment for making cheese, whatever the scale, with lower temperatures for storing and maturing (see later).

Plan of a Small Commercial Milk Handling and Yoghurt Making Dairy

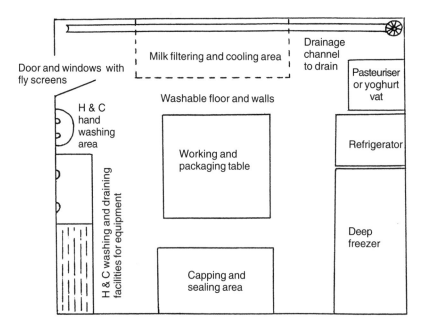

Plan of a Small Commercial Cheese Dairy

It has three areas for production, drying and maturing.

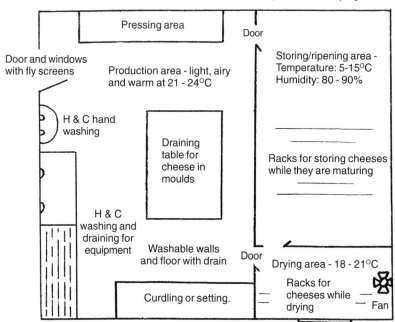

The Kitchen as Dairy

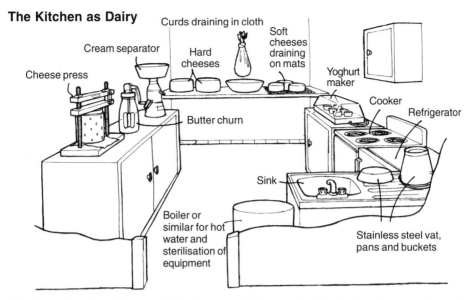

This shows the various dairying activities that can easily be carried out in a kitchen, but obviously not all those indicated here will be taking place at the same time. A pantry or utility room can also be used.

For commercial production, plans for a typical milk handling and yoghurt dairy, and for a cheese dairy, are indicated on the left. In the latter, the production area is divided into three sections - *curdling, draining* and *pressing*. The curdling area is where milk is treated with 'starter' and rennet. The draining area, as the name indicates, is where cheeses are draining on mats on a table or in a suspended cloth. The pressing area is where cheeses are in moulds in a cheese press.

The drying area is where cheeses are stored while they dry off after draining or pressing. The temperature here is normally between 18-21°C. A fan is often used to provide dry air.

In the ripening or maturing area, slatted shelving is used because it allows air to circulate between the cheeses. The temperature here is between 5-15°C, depending on the type of cheese. Soft, blue-veined cheeses, for example, will require a higher humidity and lower temperature than white-moulded ones. Details of requirements in this respect are given with individual cheese recipes, but temperatures may vary between 5-15°C, with humidity between 80-90%. As referred to earlier, a pantry or utility room can be used for storing home cheeses.

In commercial dairies, the floors and walls will be easy to wash down, with a floor drain to take away the water. Doors and windows will be equipped with fly screens, and the staff will be wearing protective overalls, headgear and rubber boots. This all helps to ensure that hygienic requirements are being met, and the cheeses or other dairy products are of the highest quality.

Milking on a Small Scale

The family milk supply may come from a hand-milked animal but milking machines are essential for commercial enterprises. Milking machines are available for a small number of cows, goats or dairy ewes, as well as for larger herds. With milking machines the milk goes straight from the animal, via the teat cluster pipes, into the containers or jars so that there is no contamination from the outside.

The milking parlour at a commercial goat farm where cheese, yoghurt and ice cream are made for sale.

Structure of the Udder

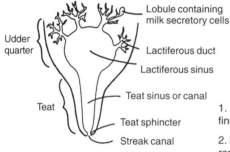

Lobule containing milk secretory cells

Udder quarter

Lactiferous duct

Lactiferous sinus

Teat sinus or canal

Teat

Teat sphincter

Streak canal

Handmilking sequence

1
2
3

1. Wash the udder then exert pressure with index finger and thumb.

2. Maintain pressure here while squeezing teat with remaining fingers and hand.

3. Release pressure and allow teat canal to fill up again. Discard the foremilk then milk into a stainless steel milking bucket.

Maintaining a Healthy Udder

Use a strip cup to examine the foremilk. Clots in the milk may indicate mastitis.

After milking dip the teats in a proprietary 'teat dip'.

Treating Mastitis

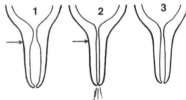

Section of plastic tube inserted into the teat canal

Antibiotic intramammary tube.

All milk must be discarded during and for a stated withdrawal time where antibiotics are used.

Milk

The milk of human kindness.
(William Shakespeare. Macbeth)

Dairy animals have been kept for the provision of milk since the beginning of recorded history. The range of animals has included cows, goats, sheep, buffaloes, asses and mares, to mention but a few. The main providers, these days, are cows, goats and sheep.

Milk quality

Milk quality needs to be of a high order for producing dairy products. It is a perfect medium for the growth of harmful bacteria, as well as the necessary ones. Those who are producing raw milk for sale or for the production of unpasteurised cheeses will be testing their milk quality on a regular basis, as well as meeting the stringent requirements of the health regulations.

The home milk producer needs to be just as scrupulous in the care of their dairy animals, as well as in the treatment and handling of the milk. Taints in the milk can be the result of animals eating certain pasture weeds, or of storing the milk next to unsuitable materials.

Where a dairy animal has had mastitis requiring antibiotic treatment, there is a withdrawal period where the milk must be discarded until any antibiotic residues have gone from the system. Commercial cheesemakers who buy in milk need to ascertain that their supplier is meeting the regulations in this way for it is not unknown for there to be laxness. Any remaining antibiotic in the milk would obviously inhibit the growth of the necessary bacterial cultures during the process of cheese or yoghurt making.

Cows' milk

Cows' milk is one of the most complete foods available, containing a wide range of nutrients. The composition varies slightly depending upon the breed of dairy animal, its genetic make-up (whether it comes from a good milking strain), and the period of its lactation. There is also a variation between the first and last milking or 'stripping' with the highest concentration of fat being obtained at the end of the milking.

Milk is an incredibly complex substance, made up of approximately 12.5% solids in 87.5% water. The solids include fats, proteins, sugar, minerals and vitamins. Milk fats are a mixture of triglycerides, made up of unsaturated and saturated fatty acids. Milk proteins are derived from amino-acids and include casein, albumin, lecithin, globulin and fibrin, although casein is present in the greatest amount and is the key component in cheesemaking. There is only one milk carbohydrate in the form of the sugar, lactose. Finally, the ash or residual content of milk contains a range of minerals and vitamins.

The natural colour of cows' milk varies from a bluish-white to a creamish-yellow. It varies depending on the amount of fats and non-fat solids. The pigment carotene from green foods such as grass will increase the yellowish colour, and this is often noticeable when cows go out to pasture in spring after winter confinement. The Channel Islands breeds can transfer more carotene from their feed to the milk. This, together with a higher fat content and larger fat globules, gives the characteristic deep yellow colour to Jersey and Guernsey milk.

Goats' milk

Goats' milk is white, slightly opaque and if produced in hygienic conditions from healthy well-fed goats, has no taints or odours. Unlike cows, goats do not transfer carotene from grass to milk. As a result, products such as butter are white rather than yellow, unless colouring is used.

The natural acidity of goats' milk is higher than that of cows' milk. It has a pH value of 6.4 compared with pH 6.7 for cows' milk. (The lower the pH, the higher the acidity). This higher acidity can cause more rapid souring. There is also a higher proportion of the fatty acids, caproic, caprilic and capric acids.

Although breeds such as the Anglo-Nubian generally have relatively high protein and butterfat levels, often exceeding some breeds of cow, most goats tend to have less protein and butterfat in their milk, a factor which can lead to difficulty in producing thick yoghurt, for example, so that dried milk may have to be added.

The butterfat is suspended in the milk as an emulsion. Fat particles are generally smaller than those of cows' milk bringing about suspension throughout the milk instead of forming a layer at the top. Goats' milk is thus easier to digest and is especially useful for those who are allergic to cows' milk. It also freezes well.

Ewes' milk

The milk from dairy ewes also has small fat particles that are suspended as an emulsion in the milk. It lacks carotene and as a result it is pure white, although pressed cheeses do attain a pale yellow colour during the process of manufacture.

Protein and butterfat levels are considerably higher, however, making the milk particularly suitable for yoghurt and cheese production. The whey also has a higher than normal level of non-casein proteins which makes it ideal for the production of ricotta or whey cheese. As with goats' milk, it produces a fairly soft curd which needs careful handling as well as generally lower temperatures.

Milk treatment

Once milk has been taken from the dairy animal there are various processes through which it must pass. These processes are the same regardless of the scale of operations; it is merely the equipment which varies.

Filtering

The milk is first filtered. With a small amount for the household, a fine mesh nylon kitchen strainer will suffice. Make sure it is the finest available and that it is high grade polythene. It is easy to clean and sterilise because it can withstand boiling water. With larger quantities of milk, a purpose-made filtering unit is available from suppliers. Where animals are machine-milked, the milk from each animal goes along pipes from the teat cluster, straight into a glass jar so that the milk is not exposed to the outside air. This system also allows records of lactation to be kept for each dairy animal.

Cooling

Unless the milk is to be pasteurised immediately, it needs rapid cooling to prevent bacteria multiplying. Where only a small amount is involved, the easiest way of cooling is to place the milk in bottles or stainless steel cans with lids, and stand them in a sink of cold running water. With greater quantities, an in-churn cooler is more appropriate. Once the milk is cooled, it should be placed in the refrigerator at a temperature that does not exceed $4^{\circ}C$.

Pasteurisation

Milk is pasteurised to kill off unwanted bacteria. There are several methods of doing this, depending on the scale of operations and what the milk is to be used for. In cheesemaking, for example, the pasteurisation temperature is normally lower so that there is less curd damage. Pasteurisation methods are as follows:

> Method 1: Heat to $66^{\circ}C$ and maintain for 30 minutes.
> Method 2: Heat to $72^{\circ}C$ and maintain for 15 seconds.
> Method 3: Heat to $82^{\circ}C$ and cool immediately.

The first method of slow pasteurisation is the one most commonly used for cheesemaking, although there are some exceptions. This, and the temperature to which the milk is then cooled, will vary depending on the individual recipe. The milk may also need to be stirred while cooling to prevent a skin forming.

One of the effects of too high a pasteurisation temperature is the loss of soluble calcium in the milk, resulting in an infirm curd. For this reason, some commercial cheese producers add calcium chloride to the milk before adding rennet, and this is an additive that is allowed under the dairying regulations. Home producers are unlikely to have to do this.

Treating the Family Milk Supply

Filter unit with removeable filter discs.

Filter the milk with a nylon strainer or with a purpose-made filtering unit for larger quantities.

Pasteurise by heating to 82°C and cool immediately.

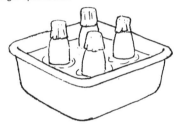

Pour milk into containers, cap and cool in cold water. Refrigerate at maximum of 4°C.

Milk Treatment in the Small Dairy

Filtering milk from the milking pail. The bucket and filter unit are made of stainless steel which is easy to clean.

A pasteuriser suitable for a small dairy.

Cheese

Poets have been mysteriously silent on the subject of cheese.
(G.K. Chesterton)

What is cheese?

If milk is left it will ripen and eventually turn sour. This is because bacteria act on the milk sugar lactose, producing lactic acid. This, in turn, brings about a separation of the milk into solid curds and liquid whey; it is the curds which eventually form cheese. The problem with producing cheese in this way is twofold:

• An extended period of natural souring encourages the growth of unsuitable, possibly harmful bacteria.

• The milk may have become too acidic for the particular cheese recipe.

The safest way of producing cheese is to first pasteurise the milk by heating it to 66°C for half an hour, so that the unwelcome bacteria are removed. Then, the milk is cooled and a culture of appropriate bacteria (a lacto-bacilli starter) is added so that the milk is ripened without needing an extended period to do so. Finally, rennet is added. This acts on the casein of the milk, making it coagulate and form curds and whey.

Some cheesemakers do use unpasteurised milk, of course, but they need to be certain of its quality and safety. (Commercial cheesemakers have their milk tested regularly). Traditionally, the evening's milking was set aside to ripen and then mixed with the morning's milking, so that it provided a natural starter.

Equipment

The amount of equipment needed obviously depends on the scale of operations. For the home cheesemaker, many existing kitchen items can be used, but there are specialist suppliers who cater for both commercial producers and hobbyists. Soft cheeses need far less equipment than pressed cheeses, and are also easier to make.

Cheese vat

For commercial producers, floor-standing vats are available, with built-in heating and draining facilities. On a kitchen scale, a double-boiler on the hob can be used. This is where a container of milk is placed in a water-bath so that water around the inner pan ensures that any temperature changes are gradual. The outer pan for the water can be aluminium but the inner container with the milk should be stainless steel.

Small Scale Cheesemaking Equipment

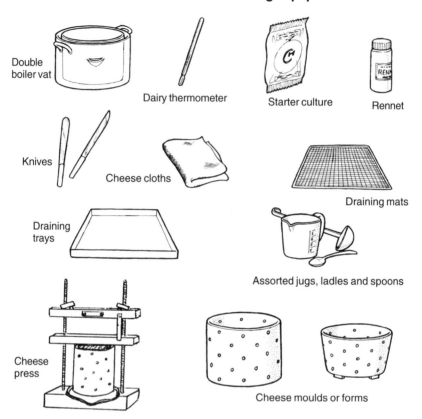

Double boiler vat

Dairy thermometer

Starter culture

Rennet

Knives

Cheese cloths

Draining mats

Draining trays

Assorted jugs, ladles and spoons

Cheese press

Cheese moulds or forms

A Range of Cheese Moulds, Draining Mats and Trays

Soft cheeses do not require as many items as a pressed cheese.
The average kitchen will also contain many suitable utensils for cheesemaking.

Types of Vat for Making Cheese

Inside a small cheesemaking dairy, showing the vat that is used to make the cheese. The lady is holding some curd cutters.

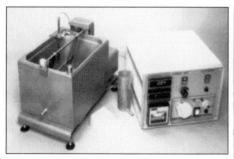

A 10-litre capacity, jacketed vat designed for educational purposes, to provide practical training in the production of cheese.

(Photo: Armfield)

On a small scale, a double boiler of one pan inside the other can be used for making cheese. See also the slightly larger home vat on page 40.

Cheese Presses

Above

The Wheeler cheese press manufactured in Devon is ideal for small-scale cheesemaking.

It is made of stainless steel and beech wood.

On the left of the picture are the wooden followers. The round one goes on top of the cheese in the mould, while the square one goes on top of that so that pressure can be exerted on the cheese.

The dish at the front goes under the cheese mould so that the liquid whey is caught.

Pressure is exerted by pressing down on the top bar and adjusting the two metal 'stops' on either side. This effectively locks the bar into position and prevents it going back.

There is a gauge at the top right of the press, which indicates the amount of pressure being exerted - up to a maximum of 50lb for the regular version and up to 80lb for the version with heavy duty springs.

Above

A traditional press made of cast iron.
Several cheeses can be pressed at a time.
(Modern gang presses have the moulds placed in a row horizontally).

Each of the high-density plastic moulds has a beech wood follower, and pressure is exerted by turning the screw at the top of the press.

This press is currently being used by a small cheesemaking dairy in Herefordshire.

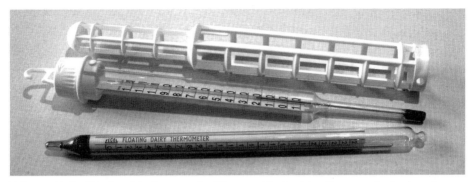

Different kinds of floating dairy thermometer. The one at the back has its own protective 'cage'.

Dairy thermometer

This really is essential. You need to be able to notice even slight variations in temperature. There are floating thermometers, as well as those which attach via a bracket to the wall of the vat.

Knives for cutting curd

Curd knives are available from suppliers but a long palette knife will do just as well if the scale of operations is small.

Cheese cloth

This is a close-textured, muslin-type cloth for draining curds. It has a close weave ensuring that the fat particles are not lost. It is also used for lining moulds before curd is put in for pressing, as well as for bandaging pressed cheeses before they go into storage.

Cheese moulds

An alternative name for a cheese mould is a *form,* and some people use this word to distinguish between the containers and the moulds which grow on some cheeses. Moulds are available in different shapes and sizes for soft and pressed cheeses, in stainless steel or high density food-grade plastic.

Traditionally, each cheese has its own type of mould, suitable for its production method and final appearance, eg, Coulommier, Camembert, Colwick.

Traditional curd knife used for making vertical and horizontal cuts so that cubes of curd are produced. On a small scale, a long palette knife can be used.

Cheese mats and trays

Purpose-made plastic cheese mats are available. Trays are also necessary when whey is draining away from the cheeses.

Cheese press

This is a must for hard cheesemaking. There are several small presses on the market, as well as larger ones for commercial use. My favourite is the Wheeler press. It is simple and effective to use, and I have used mine for many years.

Many farmhouse cheeses are still being produced on presses which were used before the last war. For a reasonably large commercial enterprise, a gang press where several cheeses are being pressed at the same time, is the most suitable.

Miscellaneous

Also necessary will be miscellaneous items such as measuring jugs, ladles, spoons, colanders, etc.

Ingredients

Milk

This is obviously the main ingredient and may be from cows, goats or dairy sheep. There are also some who use buffalo milk. In fact, from the regulatory point of view, milk is recognised as being a product that emanates from these four animals.

Dried or frozen milk will produce perfectly good cheese, as well as milk from the milkman or supermarket, although the latter will be more expensive than having your own dairy animal or bulk source of milk.

Lactic ferment culture starter

This is a culture of the appropriate bacteria which will ensure that milk is at the optimum level of acidity or ripeness before it is turned into curds and whey. There are several different lacto-bacilli strains available, depending on the cheese or dairy product to be produced. (See opposite for further details).

Rennet

In cheesemaking, it is not always convenient to have coagulation at a very acid level; some cheeses require coagulation earlier. This is where rennet comes in.

Rennet is a curdling agent which acts on the milk protein casein, causing separation of the milk into solid curds and liquid whey. Traditionally it was derived from a calf's stomach, but now a vegetarian rennet is also available. General rate of usage is 4 drops per 5 litres of milk for soft cheeses and 4 drops per 1 litre for hard cheeses, but this varies depending on the cheese. Some soft cheeses, for example, need a very small amount, with a long setting period, otherwise they go rubbery. Also, the more acidic the milk is, and the more starter has been used, the shorter the setting time. Coagulation also takes place more quickly at a warm temperature, such as 30°C. When dealing with small amounts, experiment and use more or less next time. With so many different factors there is much variation.

Salt

Salt enhances the flavour of a cheese, and acts as a preservative. It also helps to drain and firm the cheese. It is sprinkled on to the curds at the 'milling' stage before they are put into the mould. Some cheeses require soaking in a brine bath. The amounts vary, depending on the cheese, but a general guideline is as follows:

Dry salting: 2% per kilo of curds, ie, 20g salt per kilogram of curd.
20% brine solution: 200ml (13 level tablespoons) salt per litre of water. (See Page 100)

Herbs

Some cheeses may have chopped herbs such as parsley or sage added for extra taste, and depending on the recipe. Fresh or dried herbs can be used, and are normally added to the curd at salting. Finished soft cheeses are sometimes rolled in herbs or crushed black peppercorns. Some pressed cheeses may be marinated in beer or cider.

Colouring

Annatto, a substance from the seeds of the South American plant *Bixa orellana*, is sometimes used to colour cheeses, but home cheesemakers generally do not need it. It is available from specialist suppliers. The amount used depends on the degree of colour required, and usually ranges between 5-15ml per 50 litres of milk. The colour becomes more apparent as the curds form. It is added after the starter but before the rennet.

Wax

Pressed cheeses can be bandaged or coated with wax, and cheese wax is available in different colours from specialist suppliers.

Starters

As referred to earlier a starter is a culture of lactic-acid producing bacteria which provides the milk with an optimum level of acidity for the production of cheese or other dairy products. The most common ones for cheese are *Streptococcus lactis* and *Streptococcus cremoris*, while *Lactobacillus bulgaricus* is used for making yoghurt. Some cultures have a range of different bacteria, making them suitable for all types of soft or pressed cheeses, while others are manufactured for specific cheeses. Whatever the type, follow the manufacturer's instructions.

Starters tend to be of two types:

• *Thermophilic* These can stand higher temperatures than normal. They are used in some Italian and Swiss cheeses that require higher than usual temperatures in their production. Yoghurt starters are also thermophilic.

• *Mesophilic* These are used at lower temperatures and are used for most cheeses.

Starters are added to the milk after pasteurisation has killed off harmful bacteria, and act on the milk to convert the milk sugar lactose to lactic acid.

Starter cultures are available in freeze-dried form, in foil packets, from specialists who supply by mail order. They need to be stored in the freezer until used.

Commercial cheesemakers who are making cheese every day, will tend to use a range of different starters, or those that contain several different strains. They may alternate the culture every other day. This is because of a virus called bacteriophage which can attack the starter culture cells. With a range of different strains, this is less likely to be a problem. Home cheesemakers will not need to worry about this because they are not making cheese on a regular enough basis.

Preparing a freeze-dried incubated starter

An example of an 'incubated before use' starter

1. Heat one litre of milk to 90°C for 10 minutes. Put the lid on the pan immediately and cool to 20-22°C. Sprinkle in the starter and mix well.

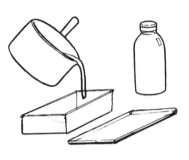

2. Pour the milk into a previously sterilised container eg. polythene bottle or polythene box and cover immediately. Incubate at 20-22°C for 24 hours.

3. When ready to use, the starter resembles yoghurt and should smell sharp and clean. This is the mother culture that can now be used for making cheese. Any not used can be frozen. (On a kitchen scale, freeze as ice cubes). It can also be propagated to produce more for future use.

Propagating the mother culture for future use

Sterilise boilable containers of milk in a boiler or pressure cooker and cool to 20-22°C

Put some of the mother culture in the milk. Doing this over a gas flame helps to disperse unwanted contaminants.

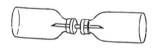

Alternatively, use purpose-made, polythene Lewis bottles to transfer the culture so that there is even less of a risk of contamination.

Note:

• Only some of the originally incubated freezer-dried culture should be used for sub-culturing.

• Add around 15ml (1 tablespoonful) of the incubated mother culture to 1 litre of sterilised milk for making a sub-culture.

• If using previously frozen, incubated mother culture, use one cube per 1 litre of sterilised milk.

• These procedures are for normal mesophilic starters. If thermophilic starters for specialised cheeses such as some Swiss and Italian cheeses are used, they are incubated at higher temperatures. These are indicated in the instructions that accompany the original sachets.

Freeze-dried starters are generally available in one of two forms:

• *direct vat inoculation (DVI) starter cultures.*

• *traditional or incubated before use starter cultures.*

Direct vat inoculation (DVI) starter

This is the most convenient to use because it is merely a matter of opening the foil sachet and sprinkling the starter into the milk in the vat. One sachet of Ezal MA4001 or 4002 (which are commonly used) will be enough for 50 litres of milk, so while suitable for the commercial dairy, may be too much for the home cheesemaker. However, it is possible, although not recommended, to use some of the powder, then re-seal the sachet with tape and freeze it until next time. It is emphasised that this saving procedure is for home users only; it is not recommended for commercial production. It cannot be incubated to make more starter.

The general guidelines as to its usage are as follows:

> **Soft cheese**: Leave to ripen for 30 minutes
> **Hard cheese**: Leave for 60 minutes before adding rennet

Traditional or incubated before use starters

As the name suggests, these are freeze-dried cultures that need to be incubated before use. Some of the most common are Ezal MM100 and 101, but there are many others. The procedure for preparing them is as follows:

Heat one litre of fresh milk to 90°C for ten minutes. Put the saucepan lid on immediately and allow the milk to cool to 20-22°C. The simplest way of doing this is to place the saucepan in cold water for a short time.

Sprinkle the culture from the sachet into the cooled, sterilised milk and stir well until completely mixed. Pour the milk into a previously sterilised container such as a food-grade plastic box or wide-necked polythene jar, and put on the lid immediately. (Some cheesemakers use plastic containers of the sort used to hold ice cream).

Place in a warm place at 20-22°C for 24 hours so that the culture is incubated. It is then ready for use. It should smell clean and sharp and resemble yoghurt.

As to how much of this starter to use, amounts obviously vary depending on the scale and type of cheese to be made. In the recipes in this book, where liquid measurements are mentioned, they are amounts taken from the one litre of made-up starter referred to here.

After taking the amount needed for making the cheese, the rest of the culture can be frozen. Home users may find it useful to store the rest of the culture in a self-sealing, ice-cube freezer bag until needed. One of these cubes is approximately equivalent to one tablespoon.

Propagating the mother culture for future use

Some of the original batch of incubated starter, often referred to as the 'mother culture' can be used to produce further batches of 'sub-cultures' for future use. It is important to remember that only the originally incubated culture should be used for this, not subsequently produced sub-cultures.

Skimmed milk can be used, but those using goats' or ewes' milk for their cheeses will obviously need to use starters that are inoculated in the appropriate goat or sheep milk.

Prepare some sterilised milk by placing milk in previously sterilised and boilable polythene bottles with screw caps and put on the caps very loosely. Alternatively, cover the tops with clingfilm. Place in a large pan of water with a rack, trivet or crumpled cloth at the bottom. Cover the pan and heat to just below boiling point (simmering) then allow to cool naturally. Tighten the caps when the containers are removed. A pressure cooker can be used, if preferred.

When the milk has cooled to 20-22°C, add some of the mother culture to it. For one litre of milk, around 15ml (1 tablespoon) is sufficient. If you are using frozen mother culture, one ice cube is enough for 1 litre of milk.

Transferring the culture near a flame, such as a gas hob or Bunsen burner, helps to displace any contaminants in the air. Working above a pan of boiling water has the same effect. Alternatively, there are purpose-made Lewis bottles. These are polythene bottles with special rubber seals. The culture is transferred from one bottle to another with a hollow, double-ended inoculating needle and the bottles themselves remain air-tight. Although the rubber seals are punctured by the needle, they reseal afterwards and can be used many times.

Natural ripening

As referred to earlier, the traditional method of 'starting' or ripening the milk was to use a mixture of the morning's milking with the previous night's milking. Many people still use this method and there is nothing wrong with it as long as the quality of milk in its production and handling are second to none. Dairy animals producing raw milk for use in the production of dairy products need to have regular veterinary inspection, and the milk itself also requires regular testing.

Those who are making cheeses for sale are recommended to use commercial starters only. Home producers will also find that their cheesemaking is likely to be more successful with a commercial starter.

If there is any doubt whatsoever about the quality of the milk, it should be pasteurised before use. Scrupulous handling of the milk after pasteurisation is also required. Bacterial contamination of soft cheeses can cause Listeria food poisoning. The advice from health experts is that pregnant women, the old, the very young and the sick should avoid eating soft, ripened cheeses.

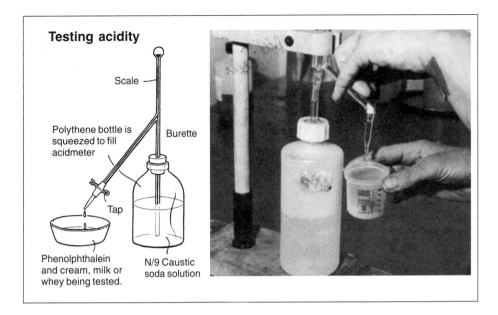

Testing acidity

Scale

Polythene bottle is squeezed to fill acidmeter

Burette

Tap

Phenolphthalein and cream, milk or whey being tested.

N/9 Caustic soda solution

Acidity

At different stages of cheesemaking, it is necessary to know the level of acidity of the milk or curds. For example, when making a Cheshire cheese the acidity or level of lactic acid in the milk should be about 0.20% at renneting. Perfectly good cheeses can be made without as detailed a technique as this, but the ability to test the acidity is important to the commercial producer if a reasonably standard product is to be achieved. On page 71 there is an acidity guide for pressed cheeses.

Those producing cheeses for home use do not usually test the acidity, but rely on experience and leaving the started milk for a given time. Those making cheese for the first time, should therefore follow the time recommendations given in the recipes, rather than worrying about testing for acidity.

One way of testing acidity is to use a Lloyd's acidmeter, of which two examples are shown above. They include a burette with a scale and tap, a container of N/9 strength sodium hydroxide. (An N/9 solution of sodium hydroxide is made by dissolving 4.5 grams of pure caustic soda in one litre of distilled water). Also included is some phenolphthalein indicator. The following is an explanation of how to test the acidity of milk, whey or cream.

Put 10ml of milk (or whey or cream) in a white dish and add 2 or 3 drops of the indicator phenolphthalein solution. The sodium hydroxide (NaOH) solution of N/9 strength is then added, drop by drop, by opening the clip of the burette, until a very faint pink tinge appears and stays in the milk/phenolphthalein mixture.

(Remember to stir the mixture all the time).

The principle of the testing is that 1ml of N/9 sodium hydroxide will neutralise 0.01g of lactic acid. If, when reading the results, on the burette scale, the 10ml of milk have needed 2.7 ml of caustic soda solution, the acidity will be 0.27% (ie, the reading has been divided by 10 to arrive at the percentage).

Acidity of the curd can be tested by checking the pH value. Dairying pH sticks are available from specialist suppliers, but they are relatively expensive. Electronic pH gauges are also available.

Types of cheese

There appears to be no universally agreed system of classifying cheeses. Some authorities categorise them according to the ripening time, whether they are pressed or not, or even by nationality. As this book is primarily for the small-scale cheesemaker, I have classified them according to their production methods.

It should be remembered however, that those who sell their cheeses must abide by the legislation governing descriptions. These cover the amount of fat and water in given cheeses. Some examples are as follows: Full fat hard cheese; Medium fat hard cheese; Full fat soft cheese; Medium fat soft cheese; Low fat soft cheese.

Soft cheeses
These are cheeses which are not pressed and which do not require to be ripened. In other words, they can be eaten straight away. Examples are cream and curd cheeses.

Soft ripened cheeses
These are cheeses which are allowed to ripen for a period before they are ready to eat. Examples are Brie-type cheeses.

Semi-hard cheeses
As the name implies these are cheeses which have been subjected to a certain amount of pressure, but not enough to destroy the light, crumbly texture of the final product. Caerphilly is an example of such a cheese.

Hard, pressed cheeses
These are cheeses such as Cheddar which have been subjected to considerable pressure in order to remove a large proportion of liquid, before they are left to mature in storage.

Inoculated cheeses
These cheeses have had inoculants such as white or blue moulds introduced into them so that a particular flavour, aroma and mould growth are produced. An example of a white moulded cheese is Camembert, while a blue-veined one is Blue Wensleydale.

This is a semi-pressed cheese. For home consumption it can be left unpackaged, but cheeses for sale must be protected by a rind or adequate packaging.

Cheeses from a small dairy on sale at a Farmers' Market. The wedges are all individually packaged.

Packaging cheeses

There is a wide range of packaging materials available for wrapping or otherwise protecting cheeses.

Hard pressed cheeses are usually bandaged or waxed, depending on their size, while semi-pressed cheeses are often waxed. Blocks or wedges can be wrapped in polypropylene clear wrap or heat-sealed in vacuum packs.

As far as soft cheeses are concerned, they can be put in plastic pots with lids, rather like shallow yoghurt pots. Polypropylene clear wrap, clingfilm and proprietary waxed paper are also used. Wood chip boxes are also available as outside packaging for speciality cheeses such as Brie and Camembert-type cheeses.

As far as the home cheesemaker is concerned, these materials are also available from specialist suppliers, although it may not always be easy to buy them in relatively small quantities. Plastic pots or small dishes can be utilised for many soft cheeses made for the family. Clingfilm across the top makes a protective lid if there is not one available. Greaseproof paper is also useful for wrapping portions of semi-pressed cheeses, with a final wrapping of aluminium foil.

Selling cheeses

Selling direct to the customer at the farmgate or at farmers' markets are the best avenues of sale for the small producer. The premises must be registered and are subject to inspection. See Appendix I for further information on the regulations.

Step-by-step cheesemaking

There is very good cheese as well as bad made in Suffolk
(Thomas Tusser. Five Hundred Points of Good Husbandry. 1557)

If you are making cheeses for the first time, don't expect to save money by making your own, unless you have your own milk supply and are doing it on a fairly large scale. To make half a kilo of cheese, for example, will need around four litres of milk.

The second piece of advice is to start with a soft cheese and gain experience with that technique before going on to hard cheese production.

Thirdly, use a commercial starter and rennet, for the results will be more reliable and consistent.

Finally, do keep a record of all your cheesemaking activities in a Cheese Log Book (an ordinary hardback notebook will do). In this way it is possible to reproduce a particularly good cheese again, as well as avoiding faults that may have shown up the first time.

Soft cheese

Every soft cheese is different and the production methods will vary depending on the recipe. The simplest is a pot cheese.

Pot cheese

2.5 litres milk
10ml (2 teaspoons) liquid starter or a little DVI starter
2 drops rennet
Salt and flavourings to taste

Pasteurise the milk by heating to 66°C for 30 minutes, then allow to cool to 30°C. Check the temperatures with a dairy thermometer. Add the starter and stir in well. Cover the pan and leave in a warm place for half an hour.

Mix the rennet with two teaspoonfuls of previously boiled and cooled water, then stir into the milk. Cover the pan and leave in a warm place until the milk has set into a curd.

Drain off as much of the liquid whey as possible, then ladle the curd into a cheese cloth placed in a colander. Make the cloth into a bag and hang up to drain for around 24 hours. Once the whey has drained away, scrape the curd from the cloth and place in a dish. Add salt, pepper or other flavour, as desired, and store in the refrigerator until eaten. It will keep for around five days.

Making a Pot Cheese

1. Pasteurise milk then cool to 30°C and add starter, followed by rennet half an hour later.

3. Make the cloth into a bag and hang to drain.

2. When set, ladle the curds into a colander lined with cheese cloth.

An alternative to draining in cheesecloth is to use a mould in a tray.

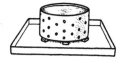

Keep the mould covered while draining is taking place

Soft cheese in a mould, eg, Coulommier

Coulommier is a soft cheese from France that is produced in a mould rather than in a draining cloth. Purpose-made, stainless steel, Coulommier moulds, such as the one shown here, are available. Two plastic, open-ended moulds can also be used, one on top of another. Masking tape can then be used to hold these together until the two halves are separated.

When my grandchildren want to make cheese with me, this is the recipe I use.

3 litres milk
5ml liquid starter or a little DVI
3 drops rennet

To pasteurise the milk, heat it to 66°C. Cool to 30°C if you are using cows' milk. For goats' or ewes' milk, reduce the temperature to 28°C.

Add the starter and stir in thoroughly. Cover and leave in a warm place for 30 minutes.

Add the rennet which has been diluted in four times its volume of previously boiled and cooled water. Stir and leave until the curd is firm and does not leave a milky stain on the back of your finger. Meanwhile, sterilise the cheese mats and moulds with boiling water and place them on the tray.

A two-part Coulommier mould made of stainless steel. The two halves click together at the 'collar'.

When the curd is set, ladle it gently into the mould until it is full. Cover and leave in a warm place until the curd has sunk to below the collar mark where the two halves of the mould interlock, then remove the top half.

The shrinking will take several hours and during this time keep the mould covered with the second mat. The curd firms as it shrinks, and as soon as it is firm enough, turn the cheese onto the second mat.

By the following day, the curd should have shrunk to half way down the mould and will be firm enough to remove from the mould.

Sprinkle it with salt and place it in the refrigerator for a few hours to cool. At this stage, it is ready to eat or it can be allowed to ripen for up to three days so that it develops more flavour.

If necessary, it can be flavoured with crushed garlic, black pepper, parsley or other herbs. If you're feeling in a celebratory mood, the traditional wine to drink with a Coulommier cheese is Nuits St. George (but not for the grandchildren!)

The diagrams below show the steps in making a Coulommier cheese using a traditional two-part mould, while the photographic sequence on the right shows how I have used a single, taller mould with a lid.

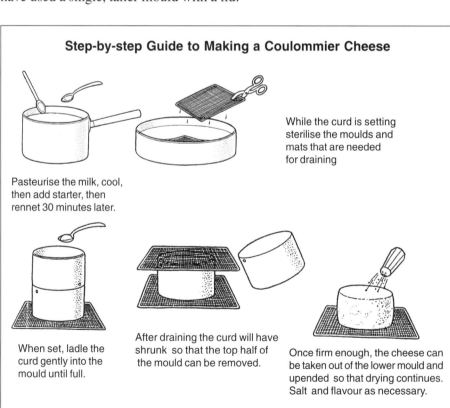

Step-by-step Guide to Making a Coulommier Cheese

While the curd is setting sterilise the moulds and mats that are needed for draining

Pasteurise the milk, cool, then add starter, then rennet 30 minutes later.

When set, ladle the curd gently into the mould until full.

After draining the curd will have shrunk so that the top half of the mould can be removed.

Once firm enough, the cheese can be taken out of the lower mould and upended so that drying continues. Salt and flavour as necessary.

Making a Moulded Soft Cheese, eg, Coulommier

A large pan of water with a smaller milk pan in it is ideal for making small quantities of cheese in the kitchen. Here, the temperature is being checked.

Adding the starter. The little plastic spoon that comes with many medicines is ideal because its capacity is 5ml on one side and 2.5ml on the other.

Diluting the rennet in previously boiled and cooled water in the jug. A dropper bottle is ideal in case too much rennet is added.

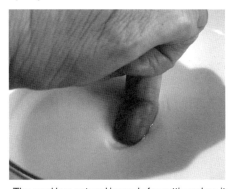

The curd has set and is ready for cutting when it 'gives' under slight pressure and also leaves no milky stain on the back of the finger.

When set, the curd is gently ladled into the mould until it is full. Here the mould is standing in a large, earthenware serving dish.

The lid is placed on top and the cheese is left to drain. Once firm, it can be removed, salted and placed in the refrigerator for cooling.

Making a pressed cheese

Different cheeses will obviously vary in the method of manufacture, with individual recipes requiring slightly different temperatures, acidity levels and production techniques. These are indicated in the specific recipes in the *Recipes* chapter.

Goats' and ewes' milk produce a slightly softer curd than cows' milk, and require slightly reduced temperatures. The curds from these milks are also normally cut into larger portions and require less pressing. However, as a generalisation, the basic steps for making any pressed cheese are as follows:

Heat treatment

This is where milk is pasteurised to destroy unwanted bacteria, as referred to earlier. For cheesemaking and in order not to damage the curd, this is normally 66°C held for 30 minutes. The milk is then cooled to the optimum temperature for the particular cheese and milk type. For example, cows' milk might be cooled to 30°C with goats' and ewes' milk nearer 27-28°C.

Adding the starter

The appropriate amount of starter is added so that the desirable bacteria will produce lactic acid at the optimum temperature level, depending on the type of milk. The milk is then left for a given time, until the required acidity is reached. If more than the stated amount of starter is used, setting takes place earlier.

Renneting

The appropriate amount of cheese rennet is added to the started milk at the correct temperature for the recipe, for it does vary. The usual practice is to dilute it in a given volume of previously boiled and cooled water before stirring it in well. Top stirring of the milk is also necessary to prevent all the cream collecting at the top.

Setting (Coagulating)

The curd is normally ready when it is firm to the touch, gives slightly and does not leave a milk stain on the back of the finger. The amount of time left before cutting depends on the required acidity for a particular cheese.

Cutting the curd

This is where the curd is cut in order to release the whey. It is first cut into strips, then at right angles to form square columns. Unless a curd knife is available to make horizontal cuts, a palette knife can used to make diagonal cuts until individual squares of curd are produced.

For cows' milk, these squares are around ½ in (1.25cm), while those from goats' and ewes' milk are double the size. The curd is then loosened around the walls of the pan and left until whey appears at the top. Again the time will vary depending on the relative acidity of the whey required at this stage.

Scalding
Sometimes referred to as cooking, this is where the temperature of the curds and whey is raised slowly while stirring of the curds takes place by hand. The usual temperature increase is to 38°C achieved over a period of half an hour, but again this varies according to the recipe.

Pitching
This is the process of giving the whey a quick circular stir so that it whirls round, while at the same time allowing the curds to sink to the bottom and collect at a central point. The heat is turned off at this point and the pan left for the appropriate time. This is usually about thirty minutes.

Running the whey
As much of the liquid whey as possible is ladled out, then a sterilised cloth is placed over a stainless steel bucket or large basin and the curds are tipped in. The cloth is then made into a bundle by tying a Stilton knot, where one corner is wound around the other three. The bundle is hung up or placed on a tray which is tilted at an angle to let the whey drain. Commercial vats have built-in draining facilities.

Stacking or cheddaring (Texturing)
After a short period the bundle is untied when the curds have formed a mass. Cut this into four slices and place one on top of the other then cover with the cloth. After about fifteen minutes place the outer slices of the curd on the inside of the stack, and vice versa. Repeat this process several times until the curd resembles the texture of cooked breast of chicken when it is broken.

Milling
This is the process of cutting the curd into small pieces. Traditionally a curd mill was used for this, but it is relatively easy to do it by hand. Different recipes call for different sized pieces but generally they will be the size of a nutmeg. The pieces are best placed on a tray so that they are ready for the next stage.

Salting
At this stage salt is added to the milled curds. 20gm of salt per kilo of curd is the average amount needed. Sprinkle it onto the pieces, rolling them gently without breaking them further. Some cheeses need to be placed in a brine bath for a couple of days. A 20% salt solution, for example, is made by dissolving 200ml salt (13 level tablespoons) in 1 litre of water. (See page 100 for further details).

Moulding
This is the process of lining a mould with previously boiled cheesecloth and adding the curd until the mould is full. The corner of the cloth is then folded over the top of the cheese and it is ready for pressing.

Step-by-Step Guide to Making a Pressed Cheese

In a double-boiler or vat pasteurise milk by heating to 66°C and hold at this temperature for 30 minutes.

Allow to cool to 30°C (depends on recipe)

Add starter and stir well. Amount varies depending on individual recipe.

Add rennet, diluted in boiled and cooled water

Cover and leave to set or curdle. Curd is ready when a milk stain is not left on the back of the finger

If a curd knife is not used, use a long palette knife and cut the curd into strips

Cut curd into squares

Cut diagonally

Loosen curd around the walls

The size of the squares varies according to the recipe and type of milk

Gradually increase temperature to 38°C (but varies with recipe)

Pitching - leave curd to settle for 30 minutes

Ladle off the whey

Tip curds into a sterilised cloth

Leave curd bundle to drain

Cut curd into long, broad, slices

Stack curd slices then restack several times

Mill or break curd into pieces and add salt

Put curd into mould lined with cheescloth

Apply gradual pressure, ideally with a cheese press

After pressing, dip in hot water to seal rind, then leave to dry

Bandage the cheese with muslin

Alternatively, wax the cheese

Store in cool conditions on a shelf or suspended in a muslin bag.

Pressing

Once in the mould the curds have a wooden 'follower' placed on top so that when the mould is put in the press there is a surface on which to exert an even pressure. Depending on the recipe, the cheese will be taken out of the press and turned several times so that pressure is applied evenly.

Pressing cheese is essentially a process of compacting the curds while extracting the liquid whey, but it is not quite as simple as it sounds. Pressure needs to be applied gradually and evenly otherwise problems can arise. If too much pressure is applied too quickly, there is a danger of losing some of the fats along with the whey. If it is applied unevenly there may be pockets of air left within the curd mass, possibly causing a ballooning effect in unbandaged cheeses while they are in store. If not enough pressure is applied, too much whey is retained which can affect the storage life, as well as producing crumbly and over-acidic cheeses.

Based on the Wheeler press, which can take cheeses up to 5kg, the following pressures are appropriate for small-scale cheesemaking. (See also page 100 for details of commercial presses).

Light pressure: 20-30lb. Medium pressure: 40-50lb. Firm pressure: up to 80lb.

Drying

After pressing, the cheese is often dipped in hot water (66°C) for one minute in order to consolidate and smooth the surface. It is then allowed to dry for between two to five days so that a rind begins to form. A temperature of 18-21°C is ideal. If necessary, an electric fan can be used to help with the drying. The cheese is uncovered at this stage and care should be taken to protect it.

Sealing

Once the rind has formed the cheese is sealed to prevent it becoming unduly desiccated while it is maturing. There are three ways of doing this:

Bandaging

A cheese bandage not only protects the cheese but also holds it together in the event of 'blowing up'. This is when air holes which have not been dispersed during pressing expand and blow up the cheese until it resembles a football. This is another reason why cheeses are stored in relatively cool conditions after the drying period so that the heat does not lead to expansion.

The procedure for bandaging is as follows:

• Cut a piece of cheese muslin as wide as the depth of the cheese and one and a half times its circumference in length.

• Cut four circular pieces to act as caps for the top and bottom, but make them larger than the cheese so that they will fold over onto the sides.

• Using lard or flour paste stick two caps at each end then wrap the bandage firmly around the cheese, sticking it down as you proceed.

Waxing

An alternative method is to wax the cheese. This is normally the custom with some of the semi-hard cheeses such as Edam or Gouda but it can be done with most semi-hard or hard cheeses made at home. Cheese wax is available in various colours from dairy suppliers and is easy to apply.

Using a waterbath, heat the wax in a pan and stir it to ensure that it is melting evenly. (It is a good idea to have a pan set aside for wax and nothing else).

Do not leave the pan unattended in case of fire! Dip the cheese into the liquid wax and coat thoroughly. It sets quickly, so rotate the cheese so that the area where your fingers are touching can also be coated. If preferred, you can paint on the wax with a paint brush but this will probably need two coats.

Oiling

A cheese can also be oiled with vegetable oil to provide a protective and anti-desiccating layer. A blue-veined cheese, such as Roquefort, is treated in this way.

Maturing

The last stage is often the all-important one. A cheese which is tasteless and bland when freshly made is full of flavour and body after its proper ripening period.

The correct storage temperature is normally between 10-15°C, although some cheeses may require different conditions. These are mentioned in the specific recipes. Slatted shelves are suitable for storing the cheeses which should be turned at frequent intervals. An alternative method of storage is to hang the cheese in a muslin bag so that the need for turning is dispensed with.

Growing moulds

There are two types of mould which are allowed to grow in ripening cheeses. These are the blue veining moulds found inside such cheeses as Roquefort and Blue Wensleydale, and the white ones which grow outside cheeses such as Brie and Camembert.

Blue moulds

These are produced by the growth of *Penicillium roqueforti* which is available in the form of freeze-dried sachets of powdered spores. A typical sachet is suitable for up to 250 litres of milk. Application is either to the milk before the renneting stage or to the curds at the salting stage.

Once the cheese is made, the mould must have air in order to grow properly. The easiest way of ensuring this, is to make holes in the cheese with a sterilised stainless steel needle such as a kebab skewer. Pierce it from side to side and from top to bottom with holes about 3 cm apart. Commercially, there are machines that do this. During this time the cheese should be stored at 5-10°C and will need frequent turning. A high level of humidity at 90% is required.

At this cheesemaking dairy in France, the cheeses are being sprayed with a culture of *Penicillium candidum* so that they develop white mould on the surface.

The famous Roquefort cheese has the benefit of the Roquefort caves in France! For the home producer, a convenient way of ensuring that the humidity is high enough, is to place a large bowl of water close by or even under the cheeses. The blueing process should be apparent after two weeks. Any white or red moulds should be scraped off the outside.

A light film of vegetable oil on the outside will ensure that the cheese does not become too dry and crumbly once it is removed from the humid conditions.

White moulds

These develop on the outside of soft cheeses and the most famous examples are Brie and Camembert. Sachets of freeze-dried spores of *Penicillium candidum* are available. They can either be added to the 'started' milk, before adding rennet, or rehydrated in water and sprayed on to the ripening cheeses later. Follow the directions that come with the supplier's sachet. A typical sachet, for example, is sufficient for up to 500 litres of milk.

Spraying can be a tricky technique, for a very fine spray is needed so that the cheeses do not become too wet. If they do, blue or undesirable moulds may grow instead. The temperature for storage is also crucial. When first put out to ripen, the cheeses should be at 12-14°C. A higher temperature will make them drain too quickly, producing a hard, dry cheese and inadequate mould growth. As soon as the white mould begins to appear they should be transferred to a room with temperature range of 8-10°C and at a humidity of 80-85%.

Cheddar cheeses in store on wooden shelving. They need a slightly higher storage temperature and less humidity than blue-veined cheeses.

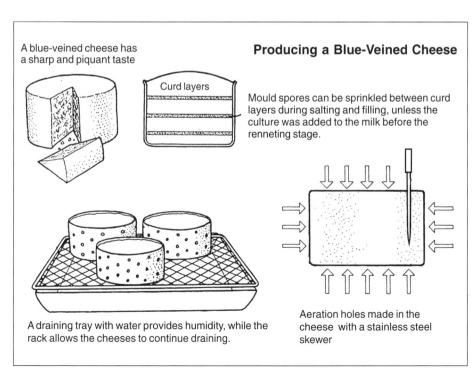

A blue-veined cheese has a sharp and piquant taste

Producing a Blue-Veined Cheese

Curd layers

Mould spores can be sprinkled between curd layers during salting and filling, unless the culture was added to the milk before the renneting stage.

A draining tray with water provides humidity, while the rack allows the cheeses to continue draining.

Aeration holes made in the cheese with a stainless steel skewer

The Stages of Making a Pressed Cheese such as Cheddar

Checking the temperature

Adding the starter.

Diluting and adding rennet.

The curd is ready when it 'gives' and there is no milky stain left on the back of the finger.

Cutting the curd

Scalding or cooking the curd

Pitching and running the whey. Here a plastic mould is being used as a strainer.

A colander lined with cheese cloth is useful for initial draining of the curd.

Draining the curd and allowing it to consolidate into a mass.

Cutting the curd into strips before stacking or cheddaring them.

When the curd looks like cooked breast of chicken when broken, it is ready for milling.

Milling or breaking up the curd into pieces.

Salting the curd

Putting the curd into a cloth-lined cheese mould.

Pressing the cheese, lightly at first, then gradually increasing the pressure.

When the cheese is taken out of the press, it is allowed to dry. Once dry, it can be waxed.

Large cheeses can be bandaged.

Covering the cheese with a coating of wax.

Keeping records

If you are seriously interested in making pressed cheeses, it is a good idea to keep a detailed record of your activities. It enables you to reproduce a particularly good cheese a second time and will also enable you to see where adaptations to such things as degree of acidity, duration of pitching and so on, may need to be made. Anyone can be lucky and produce a glorious cheese once, but it needs intelligence and application to do it a second time. Here is the record card which I produced and adapted for my own hard cheesemaking but it can obviously be varied or simplified to suit individual preference.

Cheese Record Card

Date: .... Type of milk: .... Quantity of milk: ....

	Time	Temp.	Acidity/pH	Salting	
				Amount salt	Other addition, eg, herbs
Starting					
Renneting					
Setting				Pressing	
Curd cutting				Date into press	Pressures
Scalding					
Pitching					
Running whey				Date out of press	
Cheddaring				Period of drying	
Milling				Sealing	

Comments			Type of sealing, eg wax	Date sealed
Texture	Taste	Any problems		
			Ripening	
			Dates turned	

Cheese pests

Cheese in storage is vulnerable to pests and the store room must be proof against flies and rodents, not to mention cats and dogs! The house fly, *Musca domestica*, carries disease, while the cheese fly, *Piophila casei*, lays its eggs in cracks in the cheese rind. Commercial dairies are equipped with fly-screens on windows and doors, and they usually have a 'blue-light zapper' on the wall as well.

The cheese mite, *Tyroglyphus siro*, is more difficult to exclude. It can do great damage to cheeses and the eggs are difficult to eradicate because they can withstand extreme conditions. A favourite hiding place is in cracks in shelving so particular attention should be paid here, with a continuing emphasis on hygiene.

Cheese problems

Cheesemaking itself is not without its problems, as the following indicate:

Cheese too acidic: Too much lactic acid has been produced. The starter may have been added in too large a quantity or it was left too long before adding rennet. With some cheeses, leaving it too long in the whey after cutting the curd can produce this effect, or it may be the result of inadequate pressing so that too much whey is left behind. Whey continues to become sharper as time goes on.

Cheese is rubbery: With a soft cheese the cause is often overheating or adding too much rennet, or both. Soft cheeses need only small amounts of rennet so that coagulation takes place slowly. Always use a dairy thermometer instead of trying to guess temperatures. In harder cheeses the cause may also be too much rennet or overheating, although some cheeses are required to have a rubbery texture. Most hard cheeses will be rather rubbery when freshly made because the scalding stage requires the raising of the temperature, but the appropriate ripening period will affect the texture as well as the flavour.

Cheese tastes bad: The most common reason for this is inadequate attention to sterilisation techniques and general hygiene. It cannot be over-emphasised that milk products are ideal growing media for bacteria.

Cheese smells of ammonia: Normally associated with soft cheeses which are over-ripe, it is usually referred to as an ammoniated cheese.

Cheese has a fermented taste: Yeasts are responsible for fermentation and have gained access to the curds. Make sure that dairy hygiene is practised at all times, and that no bread or winemaking is taking place at the same time as cheesemaking.

Cheese has little flavour: This may be due to inadequate ripening. See if there is an improvement after the cheese is left for a while longer. The cause may also be using an inadequate starter or not allowing the milk to ripen long enough.

Milk is slow to coagulate: There may be insufficient rennet, or the temperature at renneting is too low. However, do bear in mind that some cheeses, particularly some of the soft cheeses, need a longer coagulating period.

Milk does not coagulate at all: This may be the result of dairy steriliser on utensils not being rinsed, so that it is killing off the lactic acid-producing bacteria. Antibiotic residues in milk have the same effect. Perhaps not enough rennet is being added or the temperature is too low. Another possibility, if annatto colouring is used, is that it has been added at the wrong time. It should be before the rennet is added, not after.

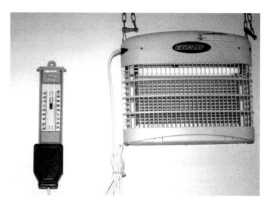

A blue light fly zapper is effective in case any flies get in. A maximum/minimum thermometer is also useful in keeping a check on room temperatures.

Cheese is too dry: Too much rennet may cause this condition. Another possibility is that the curds have been cut into pieces which are too small or have been stirred too vigorously, leading to an excessive loss of fat.

Milk curdles instantly into small particles when rennet is added: There is far too high a level of acid in the milk. Too much starter has been used or the milk itself may be almost sour.

Cheese is full of holes: The temperature may be too high, so that air in cracks is expanding. Cheeses such as Gruyere which are required to have holes, are stored in higher temperatures for this reason. Another possibility is yeast contamination of the curds, producing carbon dioxide gas which is expanding.

An oily layer on the surface: The cheese is too hot and the fat is seeping out. Store at cooler temperatures.

Cheese is too moist: Too much whey is retained in the curds. Cut the curds into smaller pieces next time. Do not heat too rapidly. (In cheesemaking everything is done gradually). In the case of a hard cheese, pressing may have been inadequate.

Black moulds on the cheese: This is caused by contamination with Mucor or pin mould. It is not dangerous but it is unsightly. Wipe it off the cheese and ensure that there are no damp patches on the shelves or wall that might be harbouring the mould. Reduce the level of humidity.

Damp spots under stored cheeses: Turn them more frequently.

Cracked rinds: Make sure that the curd does not become cold during the stacking and cheddaring phase otherwise it will be uneven in texture. Seal the cheese by dipping it in warm water (66°C) for a minute when it comes out of the press.

Cheese Recipes

Many's the long night I've dreamed of cheese - toasted mostly.
(Ben Gunn in Treasure Island. RL. Stevenson).

Please note that the names of certain cheeses are correctly given only to cheeses manufactured under license in certain areas, using specific techniques. Where I have used a specific name it refers to a similar product but is not the same. For example, Stilton should be interpreted as Stilton-type and not the original Stilton.

• **The following recipes can be tried with cows', goats' or sheeps' milk.**
Bear in mind earlier comments about the different qualities of the various milks. Where there are substantial differences in treatment as, for example, in the relative temperatures, these are indicated in the appropriate recipes.

• **Small quantities are indicated for the home cheesemaker**.
Liquid measurements of starter are expressed as a proportion of the 1 litre incubated culture referred to on page 23. The amount of DVI starter is expressed as a small amount of one sachet of Ezal MA4002 - a pinch for small quantities of milk, increasing to quarter, half sachet, etc. (Note that taking out small amounts of and then sealing the sachet is for home users only).

• **Commercial cheesemakers will use larger amounts of milk**.
The amount of starter required is normally expressed as a percentage, e.g. 1%. This means that for every 100 litres of milk 1 litre of starter will be needed. If the percentage required is 0.1%, then the amount would be 100 ml per 100 litres of milk. Recipes vary in their requirements so in order to work out the relative amount in relation to the volume of milk, please refer to the table on page 100.

• **Acidity**
Acidity at the various stages are appropriate for the larger scale cheesemaker. (See the table on page 71). For home cheesemaking, just leave the milk or curd for the times shown in the recipes.

• **Relative measurements**
With a few exceptions, I have used standard European metric measurements, but for small amounts for the home user, it is useful to think in terms of drops and spoons as well as millilitres. The amount of rennet in the following recipes is based on an estimate of 12 drops being equivalent to 1ml, but with small quantities of milk the amounts are not as precise as those given for larger quantities of milk. Bear in mind what was said earlier, that soft cheeses need smaller amounts of rennet, with a longer setting time, and absolute precision is impossible.

Half teaspoon = 2.5ml	*Rennet (approximate amounts)*
1 teaspoon = 5ml	12 drops = 1ml
1 dessertspoon = 2 teaspoons or 10ml	6 drops = 0.5ml
1 tablespoon = 3 teaspoons or 15ml	4 drops = 0.3ml

An A-Z of Recipes

The following cheeses are listed alphabetically, and include hard and soft cheeses.
Refer to the earlier step-by-step guides for further details of the techniques that are used in each case. Again, it is worth emphasising that it pays to experiment with a simple, soft cheese before going on to a pressed cheese.

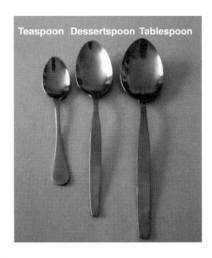

Teaspoon Dessertspoon Tablespoon

Armenian cheese

I am grateful to Peter who E-mailed this recipe from his homeland for me to try out. It is a semi-hard cheese that is usually made with sheeps' milk, or with a mixture of sheeps' and goats' milk, but cows' milk or a mixture of all the milks can also be used.

5 litres milk
5ml liquid starter or a little DVI starter
1.5ml rennet

For larger quantities:
0.5% starter
15ml rennet per 50 litres milk

Pasteurise the milk, then cool to 30°C. Add the starter and stir well. Cover and leave for half an hour in a warm place. Add the rennet which has been diluted in a little previously boiled and cooled water. Cover and leave until the curd is set.

When set, cut the curd into 8mm cubes and raise the temperature to 40°C, taking 15 minutes to do so, while stirring the whole time. Ladle the curds into a cheesecloth-lined mould and press lightly. The following day, remove and allow to dry. When it is dry, immerse the cheese in an 18% brine solution. (See page 100). Leave in the brine for two days. After two days remove, dry and leave to mature at 10-15°C and 85% humidity and turn every day. It is ripe after around 6 weeks.

Bondon cheese

This soft, fromage-frais type cheese originated in the cider-producing area of Normandy and takes its name from the French name 'bonde' meaning the bung of a barrel. Try it with crusty bread and cider!

2.5 litres fresh milk
2.5 ml liquid starter or a little DVI starter
1 drop of rennet

For larger quantities:
0.1% starter
3ml rennet per 50 litres milk

Pasteurise the milk then cool to 18°C. Add the starter and stir well then add rennet, diluted in a little boiled and cooled water, straight away. Cover and leave to curdle in a warm place for 24 hours.

The following day, ladle the curds into a previously boiled cheesecloth. Hang

47

to drain for a few hours then place the cloth bag on a tray with a scrubbed board and weight on top. Leave overnight. The following day, remove from the cloth and sprinkle on some salt. Work the curd with a fork to produce a smooth, paste-like texture. Form into the traditional bung shape and refrigerate. It is ready to use straight away.

Brie cheese

This, to some, is the queen of cheeses, but is not for the beginner to make! In order to make a Brie-type cheese successfully it is essential to have a good starter culture, and a culture of the *Penicillium candidum* spores which produce the characteristic white mould. These are available from specialist dairy suppliers.

5 litres milk
2.5ml liquid starter or a little DVI
3 drops rennet
Penicillium candidum culture

For larger quantities:
0.1% starter
6ml rennet per 50 litres milk
Penicillium candidum

Pasteurise the milk and reduce the temperature to 30°C. Stir in the starter and then add the *Penicillium candidum* culture. Follow the manufacturer's instructions for whichever brand you use. Alternatively, spray the culture on the finished cheeses.

Add the previously diluted rennet, cover and leave to coagulate slowly for about 3 hours at 28°C-30°C. When set, strain off the whey and gently ladle the curd in slices into small moulds which are not too deep. Leave to drain until the following day at about 20°C. By this time they will have settled to half their original volume and require turning. This should be done carefully so as not to damage the curd, and involves up-ending the mould onto a second cheese mat.

When the cheese is firm enough to be taken out of the mould (usually the following day) gently sprinkle salt on the surface and sides. A few hours later turn the cheese and sprinkle salt on the bottom. If spraying is to be done, this is the time to do it. It is possible to take out a little of the mould powder, and then quckly reseal the sachet, but this is for home users only, not commercial producers.

The culture is added to previously boiled and cooled water to which a little salt has been added. For home use, a small amount of powder in 1 litre of water to which 1g salt has been added is sufficient. A very fine spray is needed. Bear in mind that those allergic to penicillin should not be involved with this stage. When I was in France, a visitor to a dairy where this process was taking place had to be taken to hospital because of her allergy. Fortunately, she made a quick recovery.

Leave the cheeses to dry for about a week at around 14°C. Once the white mould begins to appear, transfer them to a ripening area, on their own, at a temperature of 10°C and a relative humidity level of 80-85%. They are ready to eat when covered with white mould, but can be left to ripen for longer if necessary.

Good stirring is necessary to make sure that first the starter and then the rennet are well mixed in. Top stirring is also necessary to stop the cream floating on the top, but then ceases for curd setting.

Caerphilly cheese

This is a lovely, semi-hard cheese which originated in the town of Caerphilly in South Wales. It has a slightly acid taste and ripens more quickly than many other cheeses. It is particularly good when made from ewes' milk.

5 litres milk	*For larger quantities:*
5ml liquid starter or a little DVI	*1% starter*
1.5ml rennet	*15ml rennet per 50 litres milk*

Pasteurise the milk then allow to cool to 30°C. Add the starter and leave for about half an hour, then add the rennet diluted in three times its volume of water. Top stir to make sure that the cream is incorporated and leave to curdle for about 45-60 minutes or until set.

When the curd is ready, cut into 6mm cubes and stir gently with the hands for 15 minutes. Gradually raise the temperature to 34°C over the next 30 minutes.

Run off the whey and pile up the curd, keeping it warm with a covering cloth. Leave for 30 minutes then cut the consolidated curd into wedges and pile them on

Here, the curd is being piled into the centre of the vat and washed with the whey as it drains so that the right degree of acidity for that stage is achieved.

top of each other. After 20 minutes, break up the curd into small pieces and sprinkle with salt. Place the curd in a cloth-lined mould and apply a light pressure. An hour later, turn the cheese, sprinkle with salt and leave in the press until the following day. Next day, remove the cheese and immerse in 18% brine for 24 hours. (See page 100 for brining details). Once out of the brine, leave to drain and dry before storing. Allow to ripen for two weeks. After that it is ready to eat. Traditionally this cheese was rubbed with a little flour to give it a good finish.

Cambridge cheese (also known as York)

This is a mildly acid soft cheese with a characteristic orange stripe. It was traditionally made in the Cambridge area and sold in local markets but now seems to have disappeared, except for those made by home cheesemakers.

3.5 litres milk	*On a larger scale:*
5ml liquid starter or a little DVI	*0.1% starter*
3 drops rennet	*15ml rennet per 50 litres milk*
3 drops annatto cheese colouring	*3ml annatto per third of milk*

Pasteurise the milk and cool to 30°C. Add the starter and stir well. Leave to ripen for 10 minutes. Dilute rennet in three times its own volume of water, and add to the milk. Stir in well then transfer a third of this to a sterilised bowl.

Add the cheese annatto, a drop at a time, to the smaller amount, until the mixture is pale orange. Leave both mixtures for 30 minutes or until set. Meanwhile scald a cheese mat, bottomless mould and a tray. Stand the mould on the mat in the tray and when the curd is set, ladle thin slices of the white curd into the mould until just over a third full. Add the orange curd and then finish off with white curd up to the top. Cover with greaseproof paper and leave to drain at around 21°C for 2 to 3 days until the cheese is about 5 cm high and firm. Remove from the mould and lightly salt. It is ready to eat in 12 hours.

Camembert cheese

4 litres fresh milk
5ml liquid starter or a little DVI
3 drops rennet
Penicillium candidum culture

For larger quantities: 0.2% starter.
5 ml rennet per 50 litres milk.
Penicillium candidum

Soft cheeses draining in their moulds. They will eventually sink to half the size.

Pasteurise the milk then reduce the temperature to 29°C. Stir in the starter and then a little of the mould culture, unless the cheeses are to be sprayed later.

Add the previously diluted rennet, 30 minutes later, cover the milk and maintain the temperature until the curd has set. Do not cut the curd with a knife but ladle it in slices into the moulds. Leave to drain at 20°C. When the curd is firm, turn the moulds upside down and allow to continue draining. When firm enough to remove from the moulds (normally the following day), rub the cheeses with salt and transfer to the drying area at 18°C with a relative humidity of 80%. After two days, place the cheeses in the ripening area. Allow to ripen at 12°C for 10 days by which time the mould should have grown. (As with Brie, the mould culture can be sprayed on when the cheeses come out of the moulds. See page 48).

Caws bach (Little cheese)

This is a traditional Welsh cheese that was made in the Llŷn peninsula. The recipe is my mother's. She used the milk from our own dairy animals, as well as the buttermilk left over from butter churning. The latter provided the starter as well as the coagulating factor. It is one for the family, not for sale, and pre-supposes that the milk and buttermilk used are of good, hygienic quality. If you prefer, use some cultured buttermilk from an unopened carton. and pasteurise the milk before adding it. A little lemon juice can also be used in place of rennet, but this will give the cheese a different flavour from the original type.

2 litres milk
300ml buttermilk

Heat the milk slowly to 24°C and then stir in the buttermilk. Stir well, cover and leave in a warm place for 24 hours. When the curd is firm, ladle into a previously boiled cloth, tie into a bundle and hang to drain for 24 hours. Twice during that period, undo the cloth and scrape the drier curd into the softer inner curd, then tighten the bundle. When removed from the cloth, add salt to taste, and either finely chopped chives or spring onions. It is ready for use immediately.

Cheddar cheese

This hard cheese is one of the great cheeses of the world. Traditionally it was made with cows' milk, but I frequently made it from goats' milk. The step-by-step stages are shown in the diagrams on pages 34-35, while the stages are shown photographically on pages 40-42.

10 litres full cream milk
1 litre additional cream (optional)
5ml liquid starter or a little DVI
3ml rennet

For larger quantities:
1.0-1.5% starter
15ml rennet per 50 litres milk

Pasteurise the milk and cream, then cool to 21°C. Add the starter, cover and leave for about 45 minutes. Heat the milk to 30°C and add previously diluted rennet. Stir thoroughly making sure that the cream at the top is also stirred in. Cover and leave for five minutes then stir the surface again to prevent the cream rising.

Leave until the curd is firm and breaks cleanly and no milk stain is left on the back of the finger when tested. Do not leave it for longer than this unless you particularly want a dry, crumbly cheese.

Cut initially into large cubes, then smaller until you end up with pea-size particles. Stir gently with the hand for a few minutes. Gradually heat so that the temperature rises slowly over a period of 45 minutes to 38-40°C. Continue stirring by hand while this is going on. After 45 minutes, pitch or give the whey a final swirl with the hand so that the curds settle in a heap at the bottom.

Drain off as much whey as possible and leave the curds to drain in a cloth until they have formed a single mass. Cut the curd into large strips and place one on top of the other in cheese cloth on a draining mat or tray and leave for 15 minutes. Rearrange the order of the strips so that the outer ones are in the middle.

Leave for another 15 minutes until all the gas holes have appeared and been dispersed. At this stage the curd is ready for passing through a curd mill, slicing into thin flakes with a sharp knife or breaking into small pieces by hand.

Sprinkle salt onto the curds. According to my mother, the traditional way of doing this in farmhouses was for two dairy maids to hold the cloth, one at each end and toss the curds so that the salt was mixed in well. (History does not relate what happened if any of the curds fell on the floor!)

Pack the curds into moulds lined with sterilised cloths and apply a light weight for the first hour. Increase the weight by 50% for the next hour, then increase again to maximum pressure. (See page 100 for further details of pressures). This gradual pressure is to avoid squeezing out the fat which would harden on the surface and impede drainage.

Leave for 24 hours, take out of the press, replace in clean cloths and put back, upside down, in the moulds. Exert full pressure and leave for another 24 hours.

Remove from the press, dip in hot water at 66°C for one minute to smooth the rind, then leave to dry at 21°C. When completely dry, it can either be bandaged or waxed, although a traditional Cheddar is bandaged.

Leave the cheese to mature in a cool, dry place at 8 - 11°C where it should be turned daily for the first three weeks, then on alternate days after that.

For a mild cheese, ripening should take place for at least three months. A longer period of ripening produces a more mature cheese.

Cheshire cheese

The Cheshire is an ancient pressed cheese with the distinction of having been mentioned in the Domesday Book, although folklore claims that it was in Britain before the Romans. (Recent archaelogical findings of the remains of curd draining baskets at Iron Age sites lends credence to the claim). Cheshire is a friable, salty cheese useful for cooking as well as eating.

10 litres milk	*For larger quantities:*
20 ml liquid starter or a little DVI	*1.5-2.0% starter*
3ml rennet	*15 ml rennet per 50 litres milk*

Pasteurise the milk and adjust the temperature to 21°C. Add the starter and stir well. Cover and leave for 45 minutes. Increase the temperature to 30°C over a period of 45 to 60 minutes.

Add the previously diluted rennet, stir to mix the cream and leave to coagulate, maintaining the temperature of 30°C. When the curd is firm and breaks cleanly, cut into 3 cm cubes, being very careful not to handle it roughly or the fat will be lost in the whey. Heat gradually to 34°C over a period of half an hour, stirring gently with the hands, but being careful not to break up the curd too much.

Leave to settle for around 30 minutes. Drain off the whey and cut the consolidated curd into 15 cm slabs. Place these on cheesecloths spread on trays and after 15 minutes turn upside down. Turn again 15 minutes later, then again after the same interval of time. Break the curd slabs into pieces the size of a bean and add salt at the rate of 28 gm (1oz) to 1.3 kg curd. Pile into lined moulds and place in a temperature of 24°C for 24 hours. After 24 hours apply pressure: lightly at first and gradually increasing it over the next 12 hours. Leave for 24 hours then upturn and press for another day. After three days, remove and bandage or wax. It is ready at 3 months, but is better after 6 months.

Cheeses just removed from the press and placed on their sides on draining paper for the initial drying out.

Colwick cheese

This is a smooth, slightly acid curd cheese, normally served with clotted or whipped cream in the hollow centre. It is not for calorie watchers but is nice for special occasions. A tallish mould such as the Coulommier mould is the most suitable, but the cheese is not turned at all.

2.5 litres full cream milk
2.5 ml liquid starter or a little DVI
5 drops rennet
Whipped cream

For larger quantities:
0.1% starter
15ml rennet per 50 litres milk

Pasteurise the milk and cool to 30°C. Add the starter and then 30 minutes later the rennet, diluted in three times its own volume of water. Stir thoroughly. Continue to top stir to prevent the cream floating on the top until curdling begins. Cover and leave to coagulate slowly, in a warm place, until it is quite set.

Ladle slices of curd into a cloth-lined mould. After an hour, pull the muslin inwards and upwards, thus drawing the curd away from the sides of the mould, then tie firmly. Repeat this at hourly intervals, until the cheese has a hollow in the middle, with the edges curving inwards.

When the cheese is firm enough to handle, usually after two days, take it out of the mould and peel off the cloth. Sprinkle lightly with salt and just before serving fill the hollow with clotted or whipped cream. It should be eaten within three days.

Cottage cheese

Popular with weight-watchers because it is normally made from skimmed milk, cottage cheese can be made more interesting by the addition of chopped chives or pineapple to the finished product. (If preferred, it can be made with whole milk).

2.5 litres skimmed milk
125ml liquid starter or a little DVI
3 drops rennet

For larger quantities:
3% starter
10ml rennet per 50 litres milk

Pasteurise the milk then adjust the temperature to 24°C. Add the starter, then the rennet, cover and leave in a warm place to set. When set, cut the curd into 2cm cubes and raise the temperature to 45°C. Maintain at this temperature for 30 minutes, stirring just enough to keep the particles separate, then drain off as much whey as possible. Once the curd is firm enough to handle, place it in a colander and rinse well in cold water, stirring gently to keep the particles separate.

Drain well then sprinkle on salt. Mix in chives or chopped pineapple and store in plastic pots with lids, in the refrigerator. Use within 5-7 days.

This can also be produced without rennet, leaving the milk to curdle overnight in what is called a 'long set'.

Coulommier cheese

(See pages 29-31)

Cream cheese

This is a soft, granular and rather buttery cheese which is unripened.

Single Cream cheese

1 litre fresh single cream
5ml liquid starter or a little DVI
3 drops rennet
Salt to taste

For larger quantities:
60ml starter per 45kg cream
15 ml rennet per 45kg cream

Pasteurise the cream in a double boiler or basin on top of a saucepan of water. Cool immediately to 24°C by placing the bowl in cold water. Add the starter. Cover and leave for three hours.

Stir in the rennet diluted in six times its volume of previously boiled and cooled water, cover and leave to coagulate for eight hours. When the curds are thick, ladle into a boiled and cooled cloth and hang to drain in a cool pantry.

Next day, open up the cloth and scrape the curd from the outside to the inside so that draining and drying takes place throughout the curd. Leave to drain for another day then sprinkle in salt to taste. It is ready to eat straight away but will keep for up to a week under refrigeration.

Double Cream cheese

Use double cream instead of single and prepare in the same way, but omit the rennet.

Crowdie cheese

I am indebted to Mrs. G. Mackintosh for the recipe for this Scottish soft cheese which was traditionally eaten for breakfast with oatcakes and butter.

2 litres milk
300 ml double cream
4 drops rennet

Pasteurise the milk then reduce the temperature to 28°C. Add the previously diluted rennet and leave covered in a warm place for three hours or until set. Cut the curd into cubes and leave in the whey for another three hours. Drain the curds and add the cream and salt to the curds. Beat to a thick paste and then refrigerate to cool and firm the cheese. It is then ready for eating straight away. If you want to make a traditional Highland version, add a little butter when beating.

Curd cheese

This is a simple and useful recipe because the resulting soft cheese can be used as a basis for making cheesecake. It can also be used as a spreading cheese, especially if added ingredients such as black pepper, chopped spring onions or crushed garlic are added.

2 litres whole or skimmed milk
5ml liquid starter or a little DVI
2 drops rennet

For larger quantities:
5% starter for skimmed milk
10ml rennet per 50 litres milk

Pasteurise the milk then reduce the temperature to 24°C. Add the starter, stirring it in well and leave covered in a warm place for half an hour. Stir in the previously diluted rennet and leave covered in a warm place overnight.

Next day stir the curds to break them up and drain off the whey by pouring the whole lot through a cloth into a colander placed over a pail. Hang the cloth to drain. After two hours, untie the bundle and scrape the outer curd into the middle and vice versa. Sprinkle on salt and leave to drain for another few hours. If necessary, place a scrubbed board on the bundle with a weight on top. The next day it is ready for putting into a container with lid and placed in the refrigerator. It is ready to use as soon as it is quite cold.

Derby cheese

This is a nice cheese with a flaky texture and originated in the county of the same name. I am indebted to Mrs. Hunt of Derby for the recipe.

5 litres previous night's milk
5 litres morning's milk
5ml liquid starter or a little DVI
3ml rennet

For larger quantities:
1.5% starter
15ml rennet per 50 litres milk

Mix the morning's milk with the previous evening's which will have ripened overnight. Traditionally this was made without a starter, but if you wish to pasteurise the milk, do so and then reduce the temperature to 29°C before adding starter. Leave for 15 minutes then add the previously diluted rennet. Cover and leave to set in a warm place (29°C). Setting time is usually around 45-60 minutes.

Cut the curd into half-inch (1.2cm) cubes, then gradually heat to 36°C over a 15 minute time period, stirring the curds in the whey by hand. Leave the curds to settle for a further 15 minutes. Drain the whey and leave the curd in a cloth which has the knot gradually tightened once every quarter of an hour for an hour.

Remove from the cloth and cut the curd into four wide strips, piling them on top of each other. Reverse the order after half an hour and leave for a further 30 minutes. Cut into pea-sized pieces and add salt at the rate of 28 gm to 1.9 kg curd.

Put into lined moulds and exert light pressure for an hour, gradually increasing it over the next four hours. Leave at maximum pressure for 24 hours then remove, upturn and replace in a clean cloth under firm pressure. Remove after two days and rinse in 18% brine. (See page 100). Bandage and store for two months before eating, although if you cannot wait that long, eat it after a month. Derby cheese is traditionally eaten with pickled onions, soft rolls and light ale.

Devon Farmhouse cheese

I am indebted to Mrs. Wheeler of Dunchideock in Devon for this recipe.

5 litres previous evening's milk
5 litres morning's milk
5ml liquid starter or a little DVI
2ml rennet

For larger quantities:
1.5% starter
10ml rennet per 50 litres milk

Mix the milks and pasteurise, then reduce the temperature to 32°C. Now add starter and stir it well. Cover the container with a clean cloth and leave for 45 minutes. Now add the rennet, diluted with 2 teaspoonfuls cold water, and stir it well right down to the bottom for at least a minute, then topstir for three minutes. Cover the container and leave for 45 minutes when the curd will have formed.

With a long palette knife, cut the curd at half-inch (1.2cm) intervals, then at right angles again. Using the ladle cut spirally downwards, starting in the middle at the top. Now turn the curds right over, cutting up any large ones, and continue this stirring for 30 minutes, bringing the temperature slowly up to 38°C.

Cover the container again for a few minutes to allow the curds to settle, pour off the whey and gather the curds into a scalded and wrung-out cloth, using one corner to tie around the other three, thus tightening the bundle for more whey to drain out. Leave it for about one hour, tightening it every now and then.

Have the cheese press ready. Scald the tray, mould, round follower and cheese-cloth. Line the mould with the cloth, then tip the curd into a scalded dish and break it up with your fingers, gently but firmly, into walnut sized pieces and add block salt at the rate of 28 gm per 1.8 kg curd. Mix well.

Pack the curds into the mould, fold the cloth neatly over the top, put on the round follower and put under light 20 lb pressure for 2 to 3 hours. Now turn the mould upside down, put on the follower again and increase pressure to 30 lb for another 2 hours. Increase pressure to 40 lb and leave until next day. Now turn the mould again and put under 50 lb pressure for 24 hours or longer. (See page 100).

Remove the cheese from the mould and cloth. Leave it in a warm and airy place for 2 to 3 days, turning it frequently to air-dry the outside, then dip it in warm cheese wax to coat all over. Put it to ripen in a cool store, turning it only once a week. It can be eaten after five weeks but improves with keeping.

Dorset Blue cheese (Blue Vinney cheese)

There is a great deal of mystique about this cheese. Some years ago one of the Sunday newspapers published an article saying that they had found the last remaining cheesemaker in Britain who still made the legendary Blue Vinney cheese. I wrote to the newspaper pointing out that there were many people making the cheese, myself included and they could come and try some if they liked. The letter was never published, of course. Truth must never be allowed to ruin a good story!

5 litres skimmed milk
5 litres fresh morning's milk
5ml liquid starter or a little DVI
2.5ml rennet
Penicillium roquefortii culture

For larger quantities:
1.5% starter
13ml rennet per 50 litres milk
Penicillium roquefortii

Strain and cool the evening's milk and the following morning skim off the cream. Put the cream to one side for other use, such as buttermaking. Add the morning's milk to the skimmed milk. Pasteurise then cool to 27°C and add the starter.

The blue mould can be added at this stage or later, at salting. A typical sachet of freeze-dried *Penicillium roquefortii* is for up to 250 litres milk, so home users (not commercial producers) can extract a little and quickly reseal the sachet.

Leave the 'started' milk for 45 minutes then heat to 30°C and add the previously diluted rennet. Leave for one hour then cut the curd into half-inch (1.2cm) cubes. Leave for 15 minutes, then heat gradually to 32°C, stirring as you do so, for a further hour. Drain off the whey and cut the compacted curd into 15cm (6in) blocks. Leave on cloths on a rack for an hour. Add salt at the rate of 25 gm to 1 kg of curd and sprinkle on some of the mould powder, if not added earlier.

Ladle into lined moulds and put under light pressure. Gradually increase the pressure over the next three days, turning the cheese in the mould daily. After three days, store in a cold room (10-15°C and 90% humidity) and pierce the cheese with a sterilised stainless steel needle. Blue mould should begin to spread after about a week, but you may need to pierce the cheese several times again to ensure that sufficient air is getting in. (See page 39 for details of this process).

Double Gloucester cheese

I am indebted to Mrs Jean May for this recipe.

5 litres fresh, full cream milk
500ml cream
2.5ml liquid starter or a little DVI
1.3ml rennet
2.5ml annatto colouring (optional)

For larger quantities:
1.5% starter
13ml rennet per 50 litres milk

Mix in the cream which acts as a natural starter as well as providing extra creaminess. (It should not be forgotten that the original cheese was made from the summer milk of Gloucester cattle which had a very high butterfat content).

Pasteurise the mixture of milk and cream, then cool to 29°C and add the starter. Stir well to incorporate it and to prevent the cream floating on the top. Heat slowly to 30°C, taking about fifteen minutes to reach this temperature. Leave for ten minutes then add the previously diluted rennet, swirling it into the milk and stirring in the top cream at the same time.

The temperature should be held at 30°C, and this is where a vat with a surrounding water bath comes in useful for there is less heat loss during the waiting periods. In 40 minutes the curd should be firm and ready to cut. Cut into cubes in the same way as for Cheddar, then stir them by hand while slowly raising the temperature of the whey to 37°C, taking half an hour to reach this temperature. Do not let the temperature go higher than this.

Leave the curds to settle in the whey for ten minutes then drain into a cloth and leave for half an hour. Undo the cloth and take out the curd mass. Cut into 10 cm cubes and stand on mats to drain for half an hour. Turn them over twice during this time. Break into pea-sized pieces, adding 28 gm salt to every 1.3 kg curd.

Put into lined moulds and press, gradually increasing the pressure every hour, for three hours. Remove the cheese from the mould after two days and dip in hot water (66°C) for a minute then leave to dry for a week, turning daily. After a week bandage or wax. Leave to ripen for 3-6 months, depending on the degree of maturity required. If a coloured cheese is required, add annatto before the rennet.

Dunlop cheese

This is a flat, round, pressed cheese from Scotland, and is rather like a quick-ripening Cheddar. It was traditionally used as a toasting cheese.

5 litres milk	*For larger quantities:*
2.5ml liquid starter or a little DVI	*1% starter*
1.2ml rennet	*12ml of rennet per 50 litres of milk*

Pasteurise the milk then cool to 30°C. Add the starter, stir well, then cover and leave in a warm place for an hour. Stir in the previously diluted rennet, cover and leave until the milk has set. This is normally after 45-60 minutes.

Cut the curd into broad bean size cubes and stir to loosen the curds and release the whey. Gradually raise the temperature to 36°C over a period of 20 minutes, stirring gently by hand, then leave to settle for a further 20 minutes.

Remove the whey and cut the consolidated curd mass into several, broad slabs. Pile one on top of the other, then change the order several times over the next 30 minutes. After this, mill or cut the curds into small pieces and sprinkle with salt. Put in a cloth-lined mould and press lightly for 15 minutes, then increase the pressure and leave for three hours. Turn the cheese the other way round and press overnight.

The following day remove the cheese from the press and dip it in water at 66°C for one minute. Put it back in a cloth-lined mould and press for another day. Finally, take the cheese out of the press, leave it to dry then bandage or wax it for storage. Leave to ripen in storage, at 10-15°C and 85% humidity, turning it every now and again. It is ready after 6-8 weeks, but will continue to mature the longer it is left.

Edam cheese

This is a well known delicacy from the Netherlands, usually recognised from the bright red wax used to coat the rounded cheese.

5 litres milk
5ml liquid starter or a little DVI
1.2 ml rennet
2.5 ml annatto cheese colour (optional)

For larger quantities:
1% starter culture
12 ml of rennet per 50 litres of milk

After pasteurisation adjust the temperature to 30°C and add the starter and colouring, if used. Leave to ripen for half an hour then add the previously diluted rennet. Coagulation should be achieved after about 30 minutes.

Cut the curd into 1cm (grain-sized) cubes and stir while gradually increasing the temperature to 37°C over a period of 45 minutes. Leave the curds to settle and then drain off the whey. Rinse the curd mass in warm water at 47°C then cut into pieces to fit into a cloth-lined mould. Apply light pressure.

After 24 hours remove, turn upside down and apply light pressure for another 24 hours then remove from the press. Place in a 20% brine solution (see page 100) for two days then remove and allow to dry. When dry, wax the cheese and put to ripen at 12-14°C, with a relative humidity of 85%. It is ready at 3 weeks.

Feta cheese

This is a soft, white, salty cheese which originated in Greece, but is widely made in Bulgaria, the former Yugoslavia and other parts of Europe where flocks of dairy ewes have been kept for many generations. It is a particularly suitable cheese to make in hot climates. It can be made from ewes', goats' or cows' milk.

5 litres milk
500ml of cream
5ml liquid starter or a little DVI
1.5ml rennet

For larger quantities:
1.5% starter
15ml rennet per 50 litres milk

Pasteurise the milk and cream and cool to 29°C. Add the starter and stir well to mix and to incorporate the cream which tends to float to the top. Heat slowly until a temperature of 33°C is reached then add the rennet which has been previously diluted in four times its volume of water. Mix well, remembering to top-stir again to keep the cream mixed. Cover and leave to set.

Cut the curd into 3 cm cubes and leave in the whey for a further 15 minutes. Line a large colander with cheesecloth and drain the curds of whey. Leave the curds to continue draining like this for about three hours, then lift up the cloth and up-end the curd mass onto a second piece of cloth to continue draining for another hour. Cut the curd into 8 cm blocks and sprinkle them with a little salt on both sides. Leave to continue draining and drying on mats for three days, rubbing in a little salt each day.

They are ready for eating after this. If preferred, they can be covered in brine, placed in a plastic box and stored for several weeks. Commercially, the curds will be drained

Here a cupboard with shelves has been given fly-proof doors to provide ventilation for maturing cheeses.

in the cheese vat and the salting will normally be done in a brine bath. This involves floating the cheeses in a 16% brine solution (see page 100) for 24 hours after which they are left to ripen for four weeks at 10°C, with a humidity of 85%.

French Goat's cheese

This is a recipe that I was given on a visit to a cheese dairy in the Bordeaux area of France. It is a simple recipe suitable for the beginner who is interested to produce cheeses for the family. It can also be used with cows' or ewes' milk.

5 litres fresh, full cream goats' milk
5 ml liquid starter or a little DVI starter
3 drops rennet

Pasteurise the milk then adjust the temperature to 22°C. Dilute the three drops of rennet in a tablespoon of boiled and cooled water and stir in. Cover the pan and leave to coagulate overnight in a warm place (21-22°C). The following day ladle the curds into small plastic moulds. Pile the curd in because over the next two days it will sink to about half its height. Cover the cheeses and leave in a warm place (21-22°C) to drain.

After two days remove the cheeses from the moulds, rub a little salt on the surfaces and leave to dry on mats. Once they are dry, after about 24 hours, they are ready to eat but will acquire more taste if left to ripen for 2-3 days.

Gervais cheese

Traditionally made from cows' milk, this soft cheese from France can also be made from other milks, as long as the butterfat content is high. It is eaten fresh.

5 litres whole cream milk
2.5 litres cream
5 drops rennet

For larger quantities:
0.5-1.0% starter
10ml rennet per 50 litres milk

Traditionally, this cheese is unpasteurised but if you prefer to pasteurise the milk, and cream do so, then adjust the temperature to 18°C. Add rennet, previously diluted with ten times its volume of boiled and cooled water. Cover the milk and leave to stand in a warm place until the following day.

Cut the soft curd just enough to make ladling possible and ladle carefully into a boiled cloth. Hang the cloth to drain. After three hours take it down and scrape the curd off the cloth and repack so that the outer part is on the inside.

When the curd is fairly firm, add salt to taste and put it in small moulds. Traditionally, these were lined with clean, white blotting paper to extract the remaining liquid without losing the fat, but this is not necessary. It is essential not to apply any pressure, however, for this will result in a loss of fat.

After two days, remove the cheeses from the moulds and leave on a mat for another few hours before refrigerating. The cheese is ready for eating straight away or may be left to mature for three to four days.

Gorgonzola cheese

This originated in the Italian village of that name. It is traditionally made with ewes' milk but cows' milk or goats' milk, or a mixture of any of the milks can be used. Full cream milk is necessary. This recipe is obviously for a Gorgonzola-type cheese, rather than the original. This is my version.

5 litres full cream milk
½ litre cream (optional)
5ml liquid starter or a little DVI
1ml rennet
Penicillium gorgonzola or roquefortii culture

For larger quantities:
2% starter culture
P. gorgonzola or roquefortii culture
10 ml of rennet per 50 litres of milk

Pasteurise the milks, then adjust the temperature to 26°C if ewes' or goats' milk is used, 30°C for cow's milk. (For a mixture of milks adjust the temperature to 28°C). Add the starter and stir well. Add the mould culture or alternatively, it can added to the curds later. (See Dorset Blue on page 58). Leave the milk for half an hour, then add the previously diluted rennet. When the curd is firm, after about 30-45 minutes, it is ready for cutting. Cut the curd into 2.5cm cubes and drain the whey. For a stronger tasting cheese, leave the cut curds in the whey for an extra 10 minutes. Ladle the curds into plastic moulds, sprinkling on the mould spores between layers, unless added earlier.

Allow to drain at 24°C with a relative humidity of around 90%, and turn the plastic moulds several times during the first day. When the curds have firmed, after 1-2 days, remove from the moulds and rub salt on the surfaces. Leave to drain for another two days, turning and salting the surfaces.

Transfer the cheeses to the ripening area at 10°C with a relative humidity of 90% and pierce them with a sterilised needle to ensure adequate air for mould growth. (See page 39). The characteristic blue mould takes 3-4 weeks to grow with full ripening taking from 2 to 3 months. A light coating of pure vegetable oil may be rubbed onto the surfaces of the finished cheeses to prevent shrinkage.

Gouda cheese

Dutch Gouda resembles Edam but has a firmer curd and is usually coated in yellow wax, rather than red. I am indebted to Mrs Wheeler of Dunchideock in Devon for this recipe.

5 litres full cream milk from morning's milking	*For larger quantities:*
5ml liquid starter or quarter sachet DVI	*0.5-1% starter*
1.4 ml rennet	*14ml rennet per 50 litres milk*

Pasteurise the milk then cool to 32°C. Add the starter, stir well and 20 minutes later add the rennet, diluted with 3 teaspoonfuls of previously boiled and cooled water. Deep stir for one minute then top stir for three minutes. Cover and leave for an hour or until set.

Cut the curds and then take 30 minutes to heat to 38°C, stirring all the time. Continue to stir at this temperature for a further 30 minutes, and during this time take out 2.5 litres whey at a time, replacing it at once with the same amount of water at the same temperature (38°C) and do this three or four times. This gives the cheese the typical smooth texture.

Now pour off all the watery whey, allowing the curd to mat into one lump. Have the mould ready lined with cheesecloth and pack the curd into it, breaking it as little as possible. Fold over the cloth, add the round follower and put under 20 lb pressure for 20 minutes. Turn the mould over, and put under 30 lb pressure for 20 minutes. Turn again, increase pressure to 40 lb and leave it for 3 hours, longer for a larger cheese. (See page 100).

Prepare a 20% brine solution (See page 100) and float the cheese in this for three hours. Take it out, mop it dry, put to ripen at 10°C and 85% humidity for 3 weeks, rubbing it with a dry cloth daily and turning it. It can then be waxed and left to mature.

Humidity meters are widely available and enable a check to be made on the humidity levels in cheese storage areas.

Gruyere cheese

This Swiss cheese has a smooth texture and characteristic holes.

2.5 litres evening's milk (skimmed)
2.5 litres morning's milk
5ml liquid thermophilic starter or a little DVI
1.5ml rennet

For larger quantities:
0.1% starter
15 ml rennet per 50 litres of milk

Skim the cream from the evening's milk and use it for something else. Mix the two milks and pasteurise if required. Adjust the temperature to 31°C and add the starter. This is a thermophilic one that can withstand higher temperatures. It is available from dairy suppliers. Leave covered for 45 minutes then gradually increase the temperature to 33°C. Add the previously diluted rennet when it is at this temperature, stirring it in well. Leave to curdle until the curd is firm and breaks cleanly.

Heat gradually to 54°C over a period of 45 minutes, stirring all the time so that the curd is broken up into particles the size of wheat. Drain and ladle the curds into cloths but do not salt at this stage. Put into lined moulds and press lightly overnight. The following day, turn upside down and press for a further 24 hours.

After this, remove from the press and float in 18% brine for two days. (See page 100). Remove and leave to dry on mats at a temperature of 10°C and a humidity of 90% for three weeks, then at 21°C and a humidity of 85% for the next 6 weeks. This higher temperature is to allow the production of gas in the curd. As this expands it produces the characteristic holes in the cheese. Final storage is at 12-15°C and 85% humidity until ready to use. It is ready between 3- 6 months.

Lancashire cheese

As traditional as Lancashire Hot Pot, this cheese has tended to be regarded as a cooking or toasting cheese. This is an excellent way to use it, but it is also an eating cheese in its own right, particularly when flavoured with sage or parsley.

10 litres fresh milk
5ml liquid starter or a little DVI
3ml rennet

For larger quantities:
0.12% starter
15ml rennet per 50 litres of milk

Pasteurise the milk and adjust the temperature to 21°C. Add the starter and leave to ripen for around three quarters of an hour. Increase the temperature to 30°C and add the rennet, diluted with four times its volume of boiled and cooled water.

Leave to curdle for about an hour, then cut the curds into small cubes, about the size of baked beans. Stir the curds without raising the temperature, then allow to remain in the whey for a further 15 minutes.

Drain the whey, cut the curd mass into 10cm blocks and leave them to drain. Cover them and leave to continue draining overnight.

The next day, break up the curd into small pieces again, and sprinkle on 2% salt per kilo of curd, (See page 100). Pack the curds into lined moulds. Press lightly at first, then gradually increase the pressure over the next two days. On the third day remove from the press and immerse in water at 66°C for one minute to smooth the surface. Leave to dry then bandage or wax the cheese and leave to mature at 12 - 13°C and 85% humidity for at least three weeks, but ideally two months.

Leicester cheese

Leicester originated in the Rugby area of England and is reddish in colour, hence its alternative name of Red Leicester.

5 litres evening's milk
5 litres morning's milk
Few drops annatto cheese colour (optional)
5ml liquid starter or a little DVI
3ml rennet

For larger quantities:
0.75% starter
15 ml rennet per 50 litres of milk
Annatto colour (optional)

Add the morning's milk to the previous evening's and pasteurise if required. Adjust the temperature to 29°C. Add the starter and leave for 30 minutes. Add the annatto if used. Wait 10 minutes, then add the previously diluted rennet.

The curd should be ready to cut from 45-60 minutes after renneting. Traditionally the curd was cut in a circular direction, starting from the outside of the circular vat, in a spiral towards the middle. Then it was cut across and finally horizontally. When cut, the curds should resemble peas in size.

Heat to 36°C, taking an hour to reach this temperature and stirring frequently. Drain off the whey and when the curd has consolidated into a mass, cut it into 15cm square blocks. Stack these in a pile and then restack them 15 minutes later, with the outside ones on the inside. Now cut the blocks in half and stack for another ten minutes. Mill or cut into small pieces and sprinkle on 2% salt per kilo of curd. (See page 100). Place the milled and salted curds into lined moulds and press lightly, gradually increasing the pressure over the next two days.

Remove from the press, allow to dry, then rub the surfaces with pure vegetable oil to prevent excessive drying and shrinking. The cheese is ready after 6 weeks but develops more of a flavour after a longer period of storage. Store at 9 - 10°C at a humidity of 85%.

Little Welsh cheese

This should not be not be confused with Caws bach (Little cheese) that is described on page 51. Again, this is my mother's recipe for a cheese that used to be produced on the smallholdings of Llŷn. It is unpasteurised but if you prefer to pasteurise the milk, then do so and use a little DVI starter.

5 litres milk. 4 drops rennet. 6 sprigs of parsley.

This is an excellent cheese to make if you have relatively small quantities of milk, especially goats' or ewes' milk. Leave the fresh milk to ripen overnight, otherwise use a little starter, then warm slowly to a temperature of 29°C. Add the rennet, dissolved in three times its volume of water. Stir well and leave covered, until a firm curd has formed. It should 'break' cleanly without leaving any ragged edges when it is ready.

Cut the curd into small 1cm (grain-sized) cubes and leave to stand for five minutes. After this stir the curds round the whey by hand, but do not heat while this is going on. Continue stirring for half an hour, then give a final swirl and leave to settle for ten minutes.

Drain off the whey and ladle the curds into a clean cloth but do not fasten the cloth. An ideal way of arranging this is to put the curds into a large colander lined with a cloth and leave exposed to the air for fifteen minutes until a single mass of curd has been formed.

Cut into blocks 15cm square but do not stack them on top of each other. Turn two or three times during the next fifteen minutes, then break up the curds into nutmeg sized pieces and add salt at the rate of 28 gm salt to 1.3 kg curd.

Pack loosely into small moulds on mats. If preferred, sprinkle a little chopped parsley between each layer of curd. After two hours turn the cheese upside down and continue doing this several times a day for the next two days.

Remove them from the moulds and place on mats so that they continue to dry. After another two days rub a little butter or vegetable oil on the outside and store in the refrigerator.

Mysost cheese

This is a Norwegian whey cheese notable for its dark colour and sweet taste.

Equal quantities of fresh milk and whey (from previous cheesemaking)
A little extra cream if desired (optional)

Take equal quantities of milk and whey and add a little fresh cream if desired. (The cream will give a lighter colour and a smoother texture.) Heat carefully so that it simmers without boiling and stir it frequently. A 'water-bath' type of cheese vat is essential to prevent the thickening mixture sticking to the bottom. Continue heating until it thickens and becomes fudge-like. This can take a long time, so unless you have an Aga that can be put to good use, the cost of heating will be more than the value of the cheese!

Remove onto a board and either shape or cut it into blocks. Leave to dry and wrap in foil until used. The sweet taste comes from the high sugar content of the evaporated whey, and the resulting cheese is nearly 40% sugar; definitely not for weight-watchers!

Munajuusto cheese

I am indebted to Mrs Helga Stewart who gave me the recipe that her mother used to make in her native Finland. It is obviously one for the family rather than a cheese for sale, although I did see a similar type of cheese being produced for sale at a small farm in Finland some years ago. Unfortunately, they would not part with their recipe!

2.5 litres fresh milk Salt
250 ml buttermilk Sugar
1 fresh egg

Whisk the egg and then add to the buttermilk, stirring well. Add the mixture to the milk and heat very slowly over a water bath, until the curds form and the mixture thickens. At this stage, stop heating and leave the curd, covered, in a warm place for an hour.

Ladle out the curds into a cloth to drain. The following day remove from the cloth, sprinkle on some salt, then put in a clean cloth with a board and weight on top to exert light pressure. Leave for three hours in this way, then remove from the cloth. Sprinkle with sugar and form the curd into a flattish, round 'cake'. Grill for a few minutes on each side until it browns slightly and it is ready for eating.

Neufchatel cheese

The best Neufchatel cheese is made with very creamy milk, and that from the Channel Islands breeds is particularly suitable. If goats' milk is used, extra cream will be needed in the proportion of 500ml to 5 litres of milk.

5 litres fresh milk
500ml cream (optional)
5ml liquid starter or a little DVI
2 drops rennet

For larger quantities:
0.1% starter
1 ml rennet per 50 litres milk

After pasteurising the milk and cream, adjust the temperature to 21°C. Add starter then the previously diluted rennet 15 minutes later, and leave overnight until the curd has formed.

Ladle the curds into a cloth and suspend to drain. After it has stopped dripping, place the bag on a sloped tray and place a board with a weight on top.

The next day, put the curd into a bowl. Add salt to taste, then knead thoroughly. Different flavourings can be added as required during the kneading process. Some examples are garlic which has been chopped and crushed, chopped spring onions, chives, black pepper or finely shredded capsicums (sweet peppers).

Shape into blocks and wrap in foil and refrigerate until used. It is ready to eat as soon as it is cold.

Smallholder cheese

I am indebted to Vicky Hartley for this recipe which I acquired on an excellent cheesemaking course which was run by her at Quainton Dairy in 1976. The steps are the same as for a Cheddar cheese.

This recipe uses cows' milk but I subsequently made the cheese from goats' milk as well. The only adaptation I made was to increase the heat to 36°C for the goats' milk, rather than 38°C, during the scalding procedure. The cheese was paler than with cows' milk, but was attractive and tasty, especially after being allowed to ripen for three months.

15 litres milk
125 ml starter
5 ml rennet
28g salt

For larger quantities:
1.5% starter
15ml rennet per 50 litres milk

This is a semi-hard cheese but quite firm and mild. This quantity will produce approximately 1.3 kg of cheese.

Pasteurise the milk then cool to 32°C. Add the starter, stir and leave for half an hour. Mix the rennet with four teaspoonfuls of previously boiled and cooled water and stir into the milk. Top-stir the milk to mix in the cream, then leave until the curd is firm and does not leave a milk stain on the back of the finger.

Cut the curd as shown on page 34 and leave until whey shows at the top. Increase the heat to 38°C over a period of half an hour, stirring the curds by hand during this time. Stop heating and let the curds settle for another half an hour.

Drain the curds into a cloth and tie up into a bundle. Open the cloth after 15 minutes and cut the solid curd into four slices. Stack them on top of each other in the way that was described for Cheddar and alternate the positions of the slices every 15 minutes by putting the outside ones in the middle and vice versa.

Break the curd into pieces the size of a nutmeg and sprinkle on salt. Line the cheese mould with a cloth which has been boiled, then press the curd firmly into the mould. Put in the cheese press under a light pressure and gradually increase it. Next day, remove the cheese from the mould and put it back upside down, increasing the pressure.

The following day take the cheese out of the mould and dip it in water at 66°C for 60 seconds to smooth and consolidate the rind. Return to the press and leave for another five days, turning once a day if possible. Take it out of the mould and leave to cool and dry. It can then be bandaged or waxed.

Ladies' Bedstraw or Cheese flower, *Galium verum*, that was traditionally used as a milk coagulant before rennet became more widely available.

Stilton cheese

Only certain dairies in Leicestershire, Derbyshire and Nottinghamshire have a licence to make Stilton cheese commercially. In fact, it is one of the few cheeses that has been given a 'protected designation origin' status by the European Union. This recipe should therefore be regarded as a Stilton-type for home consumption, rather than the original cheese. This is my version.

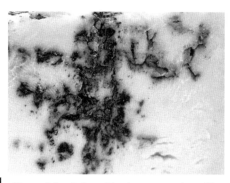
Blue veining is found in cheeses such as Blue Stilton, Roquefort and Blue Wensleydale.

4.5 litres milk
2ml liquid starter or a little DVI starter
Penicillium roquefortii mould culture
2ml rennet

For larger quantities: 0.01% starter
23ml rennet per 50 litres milk.
Penicillium roquefortii culture

Use fresh, full cream milk and after pasteurisation adjust the temperature to 29°C. Add the starter and *Penicillium roquefortii* culture (unless this is to be added at the salting stage) and leave for half an hour. Now add the rennet that has been previously diluted in a tablespoon of boiled and cooled water. Cover and leave to set in a warm place (21°C).

When the curd has set, ladle it carefully into cheesecloth placed on draining trays. Fold the cloth loosely and leave to stand in the whey for an hour. Lift out of the whey, wind one corner of the cloth around the other three to make a Stilton knot and then hang the bag to drain. Gradually tighten the cloth once every half hour for the next two hours.

Now break up the curd into walnut-sized pieces and sprinkle with salt. at the rate of 28g salt per 1.2 kilo. If the *Penicillium roquefortii* was not added earlier, it can be sprinkled onto the curds at this stage. (See pages 39 and 58). Pack the curds into unlined moulds, but do not press. Leave to drain but turn daily so that draining is unrestricted. After five days, the curd will have shrunk away from the sides of the mould and will be firm enough to remove. Scrape the surface of the cheese with a knife to smooth the surface so that any holes are filled in, then either wrap the cheese in film or rub a little vegetable oil on the surface.

Put the cheese to mature and after a few weeks, the blue veining will begin to appear. Pierce the cheese with a sterilised, stainless steel skewer, as shown on page 39, and move to a cool, humid atmosphere (7-8°C and 90% humidity) so that the blue veining can develop well. It is possible to produce a White Stilton-type cheese in exactly the same way, but excluding the addition of *Penicillium roquefortii* and omitting the blueing process.

Wensleydale cheese

This is the famous Yorkshire cheese. It can be made as a white cheese or as a blue-veined one.

5 litres evening's milk
5 litres morning's milk
3ml liquid starter or a little DVI
3 ml rennet

For larger quantities:
0.2% starter
15 ml rennet per 50 litres of milk

Pasteurise the milk if required, then adjust the temperature to 29°C. Add the starter. and leave for 45 minutes to ripen. Add the previously diluted rennet and stir well for five minutes. Cover and leave for approximately an hour when the curd should be firm and ready for cutting.

Cut into 2cm cubes and start to stir gently with the hands, for the curd is softer than for many other cheeses. Raise the temperature by two degrees to 32°C and continue stirring for another 10 minutes, then leave to stand for half an hour.

Drain off the whey and transfer the curd onto draining cloths on a board. Cut the curd into 10cm blocks and pour on some of the whey and leave for a further 15 minutes. Drain and cut the curd into walnut sized pieces, and sprinkle with salt at the rate of 20g per kilo of curd. Take care not to break up the curd too much while salting is taking place.

Ladle into lined moulds and leave overnight. In the morning, apply light pressure. The next day, turn and apply light pressure again. In 24 hours, remove from the press and allow to dry. Bandage or wax and leave to ripen for 3-4 weeks at 12-13°C and a humidity of 80% for White Wensleydale or 90% humidity for Blue.

For a blue-veined Wensleydale, the mould culture can either be added before the renneting stage or added during the salting stage. The cheese can be pierced with holes to allow sufficient air to enter so that the mould develops, as referred to earlier. (See pages 39 and 58).

Whey (Ricotta) cheese

Ewe's milk has a high proportion of proteins in addition to casein, making the whey particularly suitable for further use. Traditionally, the Ricotta is made from the whey left after the main cheese, or Pecorino is finished. There are many localised versions ranging over Italy, Sardinia and the Basque area of Europe. Essentially the process is as follows:

Add 10% whole milk to the whey, together with 0.1% of rennet or other coagulating material. (In parts of Europe this varies from wine vinegar and lemon juice to nettles or fig leaves). Stir well to incorporate everything then gradually increase the heat, slowly and steadily. The curd will eventually rise to the surface from which it can be skimmed off and ladled into moulds for draining. When firmed, it is sprinkled with salt and is ready for eating straight away.

Acidity Guide for Pressed Cheeses					
Cheese	*Renneting*	*Cutting*	*Running whey*	*Texturing*	*Salting*
Cheddar	0.20-1023	0.14-0.15	0.20-0.24	0.22-0.60	0.65-0.85
Dunlop	0.18-0.20	0.12-0.14	0.21-0.25	0.24-0.55	0.65-0.75
Cheshire	0.20-0.21	0.13-0.15	0.19-0.20	0.22-0.50	0.55-0.65
Derby	0.18-0.19	0.12	0.15-0.19	0.18-0.24	0.45-0.65
Leicester	0.19	0.12	0.19-0.20	0.20-0.35	0.45-0.65
Double Gloucester	0.19-0.20	0.12-0.13	0.19-0.23	0.23-0.5	0.6-0.75
Caerphilly	0.21-0.23	0.12-0.15	0.17-0.19	0.19-0.23	0.3-0.39
Lancashire	0.16-0.18	0.11-0.13	0.18-0.22	0.22	0.9-0.99
Blue Wensleydale	0.18-0.19	0.11-0.13	0.20-0.22	0.25-0.3	0.5-0.58
Stilton	0.17-0.19	0.12	0.13-0.17	0.2-0.45	0.55-0.65
Dorset Blue	0.25-0.35	0.19-0.25	0.35-0.38	0.4-0.6	0.85-0.9

White Wensleydale - as for Cheshire   *With acknowledgments to Cheesemaking Practice by R. Scott*

Grading cheeses

Grading pressed cheeses involves examining them at a particular stage, and allocating a number of marks for each aspect such as flavour and texture. A cheese iron or 'trier', which works rather like a corkscrew, is used to take out a plug of cheese for examination.

The following grading system is followed during the appraisal of cheeses:

Flavour and aroma:	45
Body and texture:	40
Colour:	5
Finish (outside appearance):	10
Total:	100

Showing cheeses

Many agricultural and county shows, such as *Bath and West* and the *Royal Welsh*, have a cheese area in their food display sections. Two of the most well known shows in relation to cheese are *The Nantwich International Cheese Show* and the *Frome Cheese Show*.

The Nantwich Show in Cheshire is the largest show of its kind, and takes place every July. It has been held for over a hundred years. For details, telephone: 01948 830721. www.nantwichshow.co.uk

Although smaller, the Frome Cheese Show in Somerset is even older. For details, telephone: 01373 463600. www.fromecheeseshow.co.uk

Well-made yoghurt is smooth and firm without being too acidic.

Frozen yoghurts are a popular alternative to ice cream at country shows.

Yoghurt

The sweetest and the sourest, they all like yoghurt!
(T. Robson, 1973)

Yoghurt is milk which has been coagulated into soft curds by the action of one of the lactobacillus organisms. The usual ones are *Lactobacillus bulgaricus, Lactobacillus acidophilis* and *Streptococcus thermophilus.* These micro-organisms feed on the milk sugar lactose, producing lactic acid which, in turn, acts on casein, a milk protein, bringing about curdling. The lactic acid gives the yoghurt its characteristic taste and the longer it is left, the more acidic it becomes. It can be made from good quality cows', goats' or ewes' milk and in the past has also been produced from the milk of mares and asses.

No-one can be certain when or where yoghurt first appeared, but it is likely that it was the accidental, natural souring of milk which led to its discovery. What is certain is that it has been a traditional dish in the Caucasus, Bulgaria, Greece, Turkey and other areas of Europe for many generations. Myths abound about the beneficial effects of yoghurt and its contribution to the longevity of some inhabitants of the Caucasus. Many people claim that lactic acid actively encourages the body to resist disease. Whatever the facts may be, yoghurt is a popular and nourishing dish which many people enjoy.

Making yoghurt at home

Making yoghurt at home is not difficult as long as proper regard is paid to the provision of hygienic conditions. All equipment and utensils should be sterilised in boiling water so that there are no harmful bacteria around. The equipment needed is simple; a saucepan to heat milk, a thermometer to ensure that the correct temperatures are achieved and a protected container to hold the yoghurt while it is incubating. The latter could be a thermos flask or a small shop-bought unit.

The principle of yoghurt making is to first kill off unwanted bacteria by heating the milk then, after cooling to the optimum temperature of 43°C, introducing a 'starter' of the correct lactic-acid-producing bacteria. Plain, live yoghurt bought in the shop can provide a culture of the necessary bacteria, but there is no guarantee that this will be strong enough. It can sometimes work well, and at other times, nothing happens. For reliable results, it is safer to use a commercial starter.

A convenient culture for the home user is a freeze-dried one that is sufficient for up to 3 litres of milk. Larger sachets are available for commercial quantities.

Yoghurt cultures are thermophilic so can withstand higher temperatures than the mesophilic ones that are used for many cheeses.

Making Yoghurt at Home

Heat milk to 82°C and cool to 43°C

Blend in starter

Put in
thermos flask

Leave undisturbed
for curd to form,
then remove and
refrigerate.

Making Yoghurt in a Small Dairy

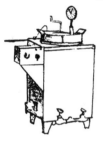

Yoghurt vat

Yoghurt
cabinet

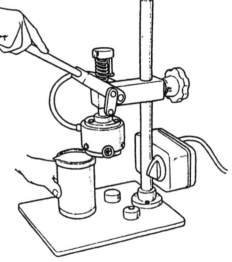

In the vat the yoghurt is made in one batch for
later transference to pots. In the cabinet, the
treated milk is put in pots before being incubated.

A small capping machine for the
individual capping of yoghurt pots

A small yoghurt maker.

Filtering yoghurt to produce Greek-style strained yoghurt.

To make a small quantity of yoghurt

500 ml full cream milk
20ml (4 teaspoons) dried milk (for goats' milk)
15ml (1 tablespoon) plain live yoghurt or a little freeze-dried culture

To make a larger quantity, use 3 litres of milk and add 1 whole sachet of freeze-dried yoghurt culture. If goats' milk is used, it may be necessary to add some dried milk otherwise the yoghurt may be too thin and runny.

Heat the milk to 82°C to kill off bacteria. Cool the milk to 43°C when it will feel hot but bearable to the finger. (However, it's best to use a dairy thermometer). Pour most of the milk into a large thermos flask or bowl which has been previously washed with boiling water.

Blend the plain, live yoghurt or freeze-dried culture with the remaining milk and add to the thermos flask. Replace the lid of the thermos firmly, give it a shake and leave undisturbed until a firm curd has formed. If you are making it in a bowl, stir it well then cover the top with clingfilm. Leave it undisturbed overnight in a warm place such as an airing cupboard..

The following day, remove the lid and leave the yoghurt in the refrigerator to cool and firm. It is then ready to eat plain, with honey added, or mixed with fruit.

Flavoured yoghurts

When making small amounts of yoghurt for the home it is best to wait until the yoghurt has been produced before gently mixing in the flavouring. Adding anything must be done gently so as to avoid breaking up the curd and producing a thin, runny yoghurt. Incorporate the flavouring with the absolute minimum of stirring. If there is a little separation, pour off some of the liquid whey.

Putting the flavoured yoghurt in the refrigerator for a few hours before use will firm it up again. There is a wide range of flavourings and it is a matter of personal taste, but some of the more popular ones are: honey, chopped fresh fruit or tinned fruit.

Strained yoghurt

Strained yoghurt is exactly what it says: yoghurt that has been strained. Doing this with a fine strainer such as that shown on the previous page, allows some of the whey to drain away so that the remaining yoghurt is thicker.

Strained, ewes' milk yoghurt is a well-known Greek delicacy, but it is just as easy to produce your own version in the kitchen. Goatkeepers sometimes strain their yoghurt in order to thicken it, if they have not added dried milk before incubating the yoghurt.

Kefir and Koumiss

Kefir is another form of yoghurt. It originated in the Balkans and is a traditional drink of fermented milk produced by the addition of kefir grains. These grains consist of dried milk solids containing fermenting yeasts as well as lactobacilli. They look like brown wheat grains until added to milk when they swell, turn white and grow into small 'plants' rather like cauliflower florets. For this reason they are often referred to as 'yoghurt plants'.

Milk is heated, to destroy bacteria, then cooled to 43°C before the grains are sprinkled on and stirred. If left overnight in warm conditions, the yoghurt will form and the grains themselves are removed, washed and dried until required for

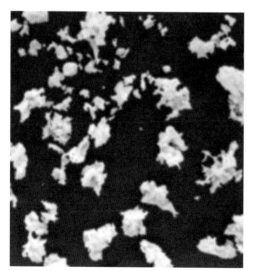

further use. They will last for at least a year, and possibly longer if looked after. If the kefir drink, rather than the firm yoghurt is required, stir it up well and leave for a further 24 hours until the fermentation and slight alcoholic content is reached.

Koumiss is a fermented milk drink that is acidic and slightly fizzy.

Starters for kefir, koumiss and cultured buttermilk are available from dairying suppliers. Follow the instructions for the particular brand, for they do vary in their preparation.

Kefir grains

Making yoghurt for sale

Those making yoghurt for sale must be registered to do so. (See the Regulations section on page 98).

For producing commercial quantities of yoghurt, the choice of equipment is between a vat or cabinet.

Vat production

Vats are available in a variety of sizes. A vat is essentially a lift-out, lidded stainless steel bucket surrounded by an insulated water jacket with inlet and outlet water taps. It has heater and temperature controls, allowing pasteurisation to take place before cooling and incubation.

After introducing the starter culture, incubation takes around 3-4 hours. At this point, cooling is brought about by a system of draining away hot water and refilling the water jacket with cold water.

With this method, the yoghurt has to be transferred to individual pots which are then capped.

Cabinet production

This method uses a shelved cabinet with close fitting door. It is popular with small producers because the yoghurt is made in the pots themselves, rather than having to be transferred later. The plastic pots containing pasteurised, cooled and 'started' milk are placed on the shelves for incubation. One model, for example, can produce up to 140 pots per cycle and needs a 220 volt electricity supply.

Once incubation is complete, the pots should be left in the cabinet for 5 - 6 hours in order to cool. At this stage, they are ready for capping and storing in a refrigerator until sold.

Packaging

There are suppliers of a whole range of packaging material for yoghurt, including plastic pots with snap-on lids, or small hand-operated capping machines for heat-sealing foil tops are available. These tops are available plain or pre-printed with the illustration of the fruit contained in the yoghurt. It is simply a matter of placing the filled yoghurt carton in the supporting base container, sliding it under the capping head which is furnished with a foil cap and then pulling the handle. The cap is sealed by a combination of heat and pressure.

All yoghurt offered for sale must have the quantity marked on the container, as well as the ingredients. The supplier's identification number will also be shown.

Yoghurt-making problems

If, despite all your efforts, the yoghurt does not firm, it could be for one of the following reasons:

Detergent or steriliser tainting milk
The effect of both of these is to kill off the yoghurt bacteria. Make sure that all utensils are thoroughly rinsed in scalding water.

Using a starter which is too weak
Use a new sachet of commercial starter.

Adding the starter when the milk is too hot
Overheating kills off the bacteria. Use a dairy thermometer.

The temperature is too low
This is where reliance on an airing cupboard or similar situation lets you down. The temperature of 43°C needs to be maintained for several hours.

The milk is too thin and has too low a protein content
With some goats' milk the yoghurt does not set properly and it remains thin and runny because the milk is low in proteins. Traditionally, the remedy was to boil the milk until its volume was reduced, so that it was thicker before starting, but the cost of this in terms of time, heating and reduced nutritional value is unacceptable. An alternative is to add powdered milk in the ratio of 20 ml to every 568 ml (1 pint) of milk. Powdered goats' milk is available from suppliers.

Not all goats produce thin milk, of course, but as a generalisation, those which produce high volumes tend to have thinner milk. The British Saanen breed, with its high levels of milk may not necessarily be the best choice for yoghurt production. The Anglo-Nubian may be a better choice. It must be remembered that it is the 'strain' of goat which is relevant here, rather than breed. The level of milk proteins is often linked with the level of butterfats so, as a rule, those with higher levels of butterfat tend also to have higher levels of proteins. Correct feeding will increase the protein content of milk, to some extent.

If you do not wish to add powdered milk; the best solution is to strain the yoghurt so that you are left with a residue of reasonably firm curds. See the photograph on page 75).

Antibiotics in the milk
When all the above possibilities are eliminated, there is one that remains, the possibility that the milk is affected by antibiotics used to treat the dairy animal for a condition such as mastitis. The effect of the antibiotic is to kill the lactic acid producing bacteria of the yoghurt culture before they have a chance to work.

Cream

Floting is taking off the cream. Some scald their milk before they flote it, and this raises the more and thicker cream.

(Thomas Tusser)

Cream is made up of small globules of fat composed of a number of different substances, each of which has its own distinctive characteristic. For example, the *olein* content of fat gives fresh cream its mellow taste, while *stearin* binds the whole together.

The cream content of milk varies depending on the time of year and also on the breed and type of dairy animal. Channel Island cows and those of South Devon have milk with a higher fat content and the globules are larger and more yellow than in other breeds. Anglo-Nubian goats have a higher butterfat or cream content to their milk than most other breeds of goats. Dairy ewes tend to have a relatively high concentration of fat in the milk, although the content varies depending on the stage of their lactation.

Globules of fat are naturally lighter than the liquid milk medium in which they are contained, and if left to settle, will rise to the surface. Even goats' and ewes' milk which is naturally homogenised, where the fat globules are small and evenly distributed throughout the milk, will behave in this way, although to a lesser degree than cows' milk. If the milk is carefully heated, however, more of the cream will surface.

Cream separation

Separating with a hand skimmer

Leave the milk to settle for 12-24 hours in wide, shallow skimming pans until the cream has surfaced. Make sure that there are no strong smelling substances stored nearby otherwise they will taint the milk. Skim the cream layer off the surface with a hand cream skimmer or ladle.

With this method it is not possible to obtain all the cream from the milk and no matter how careful you are, some of the butterfat will be left behind in the skimmed milk. With goats' milk, of course, the percentage left behind is far higher.

Hand skimming was the traditional method of cream separation and the skimmers were referred to as 'fleeting' dishes. They were solid, saucer-like utensils made of horn or wood, and later of perforated tin. The Castle museum at York has an interesting collection of early dairying utensils, including various 'fleeting' dishes.

Cream Separation

Centrifugal cream separator

Cream setting pan with hand skimmer for skimming the cream off the surface

Combined setting/skimming pan with detachable lip. When this is in place it retains the cream while the skimmed milk is poured off

Traditional Jersey Clotted Cream Maker

Plug which lifts up allowing skimmed milk to drain away

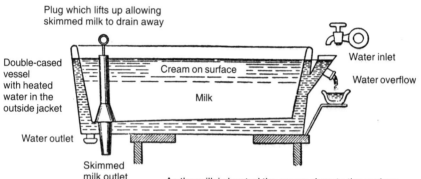

Double-cased vessel with heated water in the outside jacket

Cream on surface

Milk

Water inlet

Water overflow

Water outlet

Skimmed milk outlet

As the milk is heated the cream rises to the surface. Continued heat then scalds the cream until it forms a golden crust. It is then allowed to cool and is skimmed from the surface while the skimmed milk is drained away

Making Clotted Cream in the Kitchen

Cream in inner pan

Water in outside pan

When the outer pan is heated the steam has a scalding effect on the cream, forming a golden crust. Allow to cool before removing.

Types of Cream

Clotted cream	55% butterfat
Double cream	48%
Whipping cream	35%
Sterilised cream	23%
Single cream	18%
Half cream	12%

Separating with a combined skimmer/setter

This method is essentially the same except that the cream is not skimmed manually off the surface. The bowl is tipped to allow skimmed milk to drain away while a special lip retains the cream. Again, there are many examples of traditional wooden and ceramic utensils with this feature, as well as more modern pans made of stainless steel.

Using a centrifugal separator

This is by far the most efficient method of separating, and can leave the separated milk with as little as 0.1% of fat. The principle on which the separator works is as follows:

Milk is composed of particles of different densities. When it is rotated at speed within a container, the lighter, fatty particles will stay in the central axis, while the heavier particles of separated milk fly outwards. Centrifugal force increases as the square of the number of revolutions, but decreases in relation to the diameter of the bowl. For best results there are three factors to be taken into consideration: an even flow of milk, an even speed, and an even temperature.

The best time to separate milk is immediately after milking, while the milk is still warm and if, for any reason, this is not possible, the milk will need to be warmed to 40°C before being put through the machine.

The cream outlet or 'cream screw' together with the pressure of milk flowing into the bowl determines the density of the cream. It is, therefore, advisable to check whether the outlet is suitable for your milk, particularly if you have goats' or ewes' milk where the fat globules are smaller. It is essential to dismantle and thoroughly clean the separator immediately after use, and this can be a time-consuming business. The first centrifugal separator appears to have been invented in the nineteenth century and was hand-cranked. Hand models are still available, although electrically powered ones are obviously more appropriate if a large volume of milk is to separated. They require scrupulous cleaning after use.

Storing cream

As soon as cream is separated, the aim is to cool it as quickly as possible to a temperature of 2°C when it will store for about two weeks. For longer periods it should be frozen by putting into plastic bags, removing the air and placing in the fast-freezing compartment of the deep freezer. It will keep for up to two months in this way, but you may experience a certain amount of 'grittiness' in the reconstituted product and whipping it is not as successful as with the fresh product.

If the cream is to be used for making butter, it should not be stored in the refrigerator, but allowed to ripen at a temperature of 10°C for at least 24 hours. This allows time for a certain amount of natural acidity to develop so that the resulting butter has more flavour.

Pasteurising cream for home use

Home-produced cream will last longer if it is pasteurised. Put the cream in a heat resistant bowl placed over a saucepan and stir it while it is over the heat. Raise the temperature of the cream to 63°C but do not allow it to go beyond this or it will develop a scalded flavour. A dairy thermometer will be necessary for this. Once this temperature has been reached, remove the bowl from the heat source and cool. Store in the refrigerator until required.

Making clotted cream at home

The art of clotted cream making appears to have originated in Britain, in the West Country, and Devon, Cornwall and Somerset are still the areas where most supplies come from. Its distinctive taste is due to slight caramelisation of the milk sugar and the coagulation of some of the proteins.

One type of traditional scalder is shown on page 80. Others had one or more scalding dishes placed in the water container. The milk was left to settle overnight. It was then heated before being poured into the vat where the temperature was then held at around 88°C for about an hour. After this time, the cream was placed on cool shelves in the dairy for about 12 hours in summer or up to 24 hours in winter. The thick crust was skimmed off, allowing the liquid to drain, through the holes of the skimmer.

For small-scale production, take cream which was previously skimmed from milk in a setting pan or that from a centrifugal separator, and put it in a small saucepan or heat-resistant pyrex dish. Place this in a pan containing hot water and place the whole on the heat source. Bring the water to boil and simmer for twenty minutes so that the cream is scalded by the steam, and a golden crust forms on the top. Allow to cool overnight and when quite cold, carefully skim off the crust.

Well-produced clotted cream made from high butterfat cow's milk will be golden in colour with a granular texture and no thin cream at the bottom, an indication that scalding is incomplete. If overdone, the texture may be gritty and have a streaky appearance, or may seem slightly 'oily'.

Sour cream

Sour cream is a favourite as a salad dressing or for adding to other foods. Cream with a butterfat content of at least 18% is required and after pasteurisation it is inoculated with a culture of lactic acid-producing bacteria. It is incubated at a temperature of 22°C for 12-14 hours until an acidity of 0.6% lactic acid is achieved. Purpose-made starter cultures are obtainable from specialist suppliers, but for home production, a little plain yoghurt or yoghurt starter will produce a similar effect. If the cream is a bit on the thin side, try adding a drop of rennet or lime juice and whipping it up.

Ice cream

I scream, you scream, we all scream for ice cream. (Nursery Rhyme)

The principle of ice cream making is simple. Milk, cream and sugar are mixed with a thickening agent such as eggs and whatever flavour is desired. The mixture is heated to kill off any bacteria as well as to aid the thickening process. It is then homogenised or beaten to break down the fat particles and to introduce air into the mixture. Finally it is frozen.

Goats' and ewes' milk make excellent ice cream because they are naturally homogenised, with small butterfat particles that do not collect on the top, as is the case with cows' milk, so less beating is required.

Ice cream makers are available from specialist suppliers or it can be made with normal kitchen equipment. In fact, many people do not realise that perfectly good ice cream can be made without a purpose-made ice cream maker. I only ever use a bowl and a shallow container when I make ice cream for the family.

Making ice cream at home

The simplest mixture is a home-made and well-cooked custard, an important factor bearing in mind that under-cooked eggs are not recommended for children. This recipe is one I frequently use when the grandchildren are home during the school holidays. The step-by-step sequence is shown overleaf.

568ml (1 pint) milk	1 small carton double cream
2 level tablespoons sugar	1 level tablespoon cornflour
1 beaten egg	4 drops vanilla essence

Mix the cornflour with a little of the milk in a bowl, making sure that there are no lumps. Beat the egg until light and fluffy and add to the cornflour. Stir in the sugar, add the vanilla essence and then pour in the rest of the milk.

Stir the mixture well then place the bowl over a water bath or on top of a saucepan of water and heat, stirring all the time. Alternatively, use a heavy-based pan. The mixture is ready when it has thickened to a custard.

Allow the custard to cool. Whisk the cream until it stands in peaks then blend into the cold mixture. Pour into a shallow container. A polythene box with lid is ideal. Freeze until slushy, then remove and stir well. This is to incorporate any cream on the surface and to prevent large ice crystals forming. Return the mixture to the freezing compartment until frozen. Before use, place in an ordinary refrigerator to soften for a short time. A chocolate variation can be made by adding two tablespoons of drinking chocolate to the original mixture before heating.

Home-made ice cream is always popular. These are the author's grandchildren eating the ice cream that is shown being made opposite.

Vanilla ice cream

This is a more traditional ice cream. The inclusion of a little dried milk in the recipe helps to stop the butterfat from separating, producing a smoother texture.

568ml (1 pint) milk
2 level tablespoons sugar
2 level tablespoons dried milk
142ml (5fl.oz) double cream
2 egg yolks
4 drops vanilla essence

Beat the egg yolks well then mix in the sugar, dried milk and vanilla. Stir in the milk and heat the mixture over a waterbath or in a heavy-based pan, stirring all the time until it thickens. Leave to cool. When cold, blend in the previously whisked cream.

Pour into a shallow container and freeze. As before, remove when the mixture is slushy and stir to break up any ice crystals. Freeze again until ready for use.

Variations to this basic mixture include the following added to the mixture before heating: 113g (4oz) grated chocolate, or 3 tablespoons of maple syrup

Step-by-Step Guide to Making a Simple Custard Ice Cream

Blend the cornflour with a little of the milk to make a smooth paste.

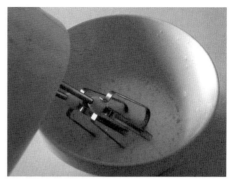

Whip an egg until light and frothy.

Mix the cornflour and egg together then add the sugar and the rest of the milk.

Heat the mixture, stirring all the time, until it thickens. Here, two pans are being used as a waterbath.

When cold, blend in the cream, pour the mixture into a shallow container and freeze until slushy.

When slushy, stir vigorously again. Freeze until ready for use.

Strawberry ice cream

This is just right when there are plenty of strawberries around, but it can be used with any soft fruits. It is true ice cream because it contains cream and no milk.

454g (1lb) strawberries
175g (6oz) icing sugar
284ml (10fl.oz) double cream

Wash and hull the strawberries then put in a blender with the sugar to make a puree. Whisk the cream until it stands in peaks then blend with the fruit puree. Freeze until slushy. Remove from the freezer and stir well then freeze again until ready for use.

Blackcurrant ice cream

This is a useful recipe because you can either use fresh blackcurrants when they are in season or use frozen ones.

454g (1lb) blackcurrants
175g (6oz) caster sugar
284ml (10 fl.oz) double cream

Put the blackcurrants in a sieve over a bowl and mash them with a wooden spoon until the puree goes through into the bowl, leaving the pips and stalks behind. Put the puree in a pan with a little water and add the sugar. Stir until the sugar has dissolved, bring to the boil, stirring all the time, then leave to cool.
Whisk the cream into peaks and carefully incorporate the cold blackcurrant puree. Freeze until slushy then stir it well and refreeze until ready for use.

Jelly ice cream

Jelly can be used as a setting agent where milk is used in the recipe. This can be either cubes of the appropriately flavoured jelly or a vegetarian carragheen jelly.

454g (1lb) pureed fruit
284 ml (half pint) milk
142 ml (5 fl.oz) double cream
175g (6 oz) caster sugar
Half pack jelly or sachet vegetarian carragheen jelly

Dissolve the jelly cubes or the carragheen jelly powder with three tablespoons of water in a bowl over a saucepan of hot water. Add it to the fruit puree and stir well. Beat the milk and sugar, gradually adding the fruit puree.

Leave to cool but not set, then gently fold in the cream. Freeze for half an hour in the freezing compartment. After this time, remove and stir well, as with the previous recipe, and replace until frozen. When serving, decorate with fresh fruit.

A mobile shop selling a range of products made from goats' milk, at Driffield Farmers' Market.

Making ice cream for sale

Most factory-produced ice cream that is on sale these days, is made from commercial 'pre-mixes' with additives such as emulsifiers. It is also possible to make quality ice cream from natural ingredients and small producers are better advised to concentrate on this aspect. Goats' and ewes' milk both make good ice cream because they are already homogenised in that the small butterfat particles are distributed throughout the milk. This is especially good for those who may have an allergy to cows' milk.

A commercial ice cream maker is essential and the premises must be registered for production.

An ice cream maker suitable for a small dairy.

Buttermaking Equipment

Dairy thermometer

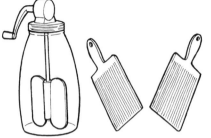

Butter churn

Scotch hands
(optional)

Mould and print
(optional)

Hand skimmer
or ladle

Step-by-step Buttermaking

Leave milk for cream to rise and skim from
surface. Alternatively use a separator

Churn cream

Drain away buttermilk then
wash butter with cold water.
Alternatively drain and
wash in a colander

Add salt to taste
(optional)

Work butter to remove
moisture.

Shape with a
mould and print

Butter

I do like a little bit of butter to my bread.
(A.A. Milne)

Butter is produced when cream is moved around rapidly until it reaches its 'breaking' point. This is the point at which the fat droplets, which up to then have been kept separate from each other by the other components, coalesce or merge together. The best cream for buttermaking is that which has a butterfat content of 30%; a lighter cream will have a greater proportion of liquid which will act as a barrier between the fat droplets.

Before butter is made, the cream should be left to ripen. Ripening is brought about by bacteria acting on the lactose sugar and converting it into lactic acid. This is a natural process and will take place if the cream is left for a time. The optimum degree of acidity for buttermaking is 0.5-0.6%, and this can be determined by the use of a Lloyd's acidmeter. Once you have made butter a few times, you will know from experience whether or not it is ready for churning.

Commercially, lactic culture starters are used to ensure that the acidity is correct, and these are added after pasteurisation of the cream. For home buttermaking, commercial starters are not necessary.

A wide range of churning methods were used at one time. Horse and dog power were utilised, as well as children and women. Nowadays, the choice of churn extends from a large glass jar with a screw-top lid, to a full size electric churn.

It is possible to make butter just by putting cream in a stoppered bottle and shaking it up. The drawback is that it takes longer, and that particular action is very tiring after a while. Some people use an electric mixer, but the difficulty here is in confining the cream in one place. A small hand, or electrically operated churn is adequate for most people's requirements.

A dairy thermometer is a good investment, for it can be used not only for buttermaking, but for yoghurt and cheese production.

Scotch hands or butter pats are used by some people for working the butter. This is the process of squeezing out any surplus liquid that remains after the butter has been made and removed from the churn. Many people find Scotch hands difficult to use, and it is certainly a skill which takes some practice to master. An easier alternative, after draining and washing the butter, is to use a wooden spatula on a board.

Butter moulds are extremely nice to give your butter a finish, particularly if you can get hold of one with a design for impressing on the top of the butter. They are available from specialist suppliers and craftsmen and the best ones are made from beech.

The author's buttermaking equipment

Working the butter to remove water.

Shaping and printing the butter.

Step-by-step buttermaking

The container should not be more than one third full if it is a full size churn or more than half full if it is a small one. In large churns, whole milk is churned, while small ones normally take cream.

Churning

Churning can take anything from fifteen minutes to an hour depending on the temperature, acidity, quantity and power source. Once 'breaking point' of the cream is reached, the particles mass together and look more greasy than before.

Straining

Strain the butter through muslin. On a small scale, a colander lined with muslin is ideal. Do not throw the buttermilk away! It is a fine drink, can be added to mashed potato or used for making scones.

Rinsing

Run cold water over the butter and through the muslin, until the milkiness is gone.

Salting

Salt adds to the keeping qualities of the butter, but you may prefer to have your butter unsalted. If you do wish to salt it, start with a teaspoon of salt sifted over 450gm, then add more to taste.

Working

The process of 'working' is to get rid of surplus moisture. Butter intended for sale must not contain more than 16% water. For working you need a wooden board such as a scrubbed bread board, some Scotch hands and a piece of muslin cloth or clean linen. The butter is pressed flat on the board until drops of moisture appear. These are wiped off with the muslin, and the butter is then rolled up into a Swiss-roll and pressed again. Repeat, making the Swiss-roll from the other sides. This is repeated until no drops of moisture are seen. If Scotch hands are not available, or if you find them awkward to use, use a flat wooden spatula instead.

Shaping

Once the surplus moisture is removed, the butter can be shaped into a pat, and if you have a pattern mould the design can be impressed on the top. Any remaining water is then squeezed out through the hole at the bottom of the bowl. Finally, the butter can either be put into a dish or wrapped in greaseproof paper.

Colouring

If you want to make your butter yellower you can add annatto either at the 'breaking' stage or during 'working', although for domestic use it is not necessary.

Goats' butter is available for those who are allergic to cows' milk products.

Butter from goats' and ewes' milk

Butter from goats' and ewes' cream is made in precisely the same way as that of cows. The appearance is quite different however, being pure white like lard. It is possible to colour it with annatto colouring. When I made butter from goat's milk, I used to capitalize on the whiteness of it by decorating it with a few petals of Pot Marigold *(Calendula officinalis)*. The bright orange petals provided a nice contrast to the white butter. Contrary to popular misconceptions, butter made from goats' or ewes' cream tastes exactly the same as any other butter, and again, is useful for those with an allergy to cows' milk.

Buttermaking problems

Butter doesn't come
Check the temperature, and if necessary warm it up a bit. Check the acidity with a Lloyd's acidmeter. It should be between 0.5-0.6%.

Butter has a fishy taste
Did you 'work' the butter on a board used for filleting fish? If you make butter in an old dairy and all the butter you make taste fishy, it could be caused by a small mould called *Oidium lactis* which lives in the woodwork of old dairies. It is rare these days so you are not likely to come across it.

Butter has taints
Make sure that the cream is left to settle in a cool place, covered up, and well away from such things as onions. Ensure that the dairy animal is not eating plants which taint milk such as too many turnips or garlic. Make sure that all utensils are clean and sterile. Boiling water should be used for all the equipment.

Shaping butter prior to packaging at a small dairy in France

Butter has cheesey flavour

The most common cause is having conditions which are too acidic. Ensure that all equipment is sterile and next time, do not leave the cream to ripen as long. Check the acidity with a Lloyd's acidmeter if all else fails.

Rancid butter

Rancidity is caused by hydrolysis of the fat into fatty acids and glycerine and has a distinctive aroma. It is a condition that occurs when the butter is old. If it occurs in recently made butter, then dirty equipment or insufficient washing of the butter itself could be the culprit. Rancid butter should be discarded.

Cooking with Dairy Products

Little Miss Muffet sat on her tuffet, eating her curds and whey.

(Nursery Rhyme)

Milk

These recipes are appropriate for anyone who has milk to use, whether it is home-produced milk or that provided by the milkman.

Milk shakes

Milk shakes are easily prepared in a blender. For every tumbler of milk use one tablespoon of ice cream of the appropriate flavour, with sugar to taste. Any of the following can be added as required: two blended fresh strawberries; 2 teaspoons drinking chocolate; one teaspoon instant coffee.

Home-made custard

This is far nicer than the instant custard mix that is sold in supermarkets, and is quick and easy to make.

568ml (1 pint) fresh milk
1 level tablespoon cornflour
2 level tablespoon sugars

1 egg
3 drops vanilla essence (optional)

Blend the cornflour and sugar with a little of the milk in a bowl. Beat the egg and stir into the mixture. Heat the rest of the milk separately and when it is about to boil, pour into the bowl, stirring continuously. (If you prefer to use a vanilla pod rather than vanilla essence, add it to milk when this is heated. It can then be removed, washed and kept for future use). When well mixed, transfer the mixture back into the saucepan and heat carefully, stirring all the time until it thickens. This makes a good pouring custard. For a thicker one, use double the cornflour.

Menyn melys

Every Christmas my mother made this to go with the Christmas pudding, a tradition that I also follow. It is made in the same way as the custard recipe, omitting the vanilla and egg, but including a tablespoonful (or more if preferred) of brandy. It makes a white sauce rather than a yellow custard.

When the Christmas pudding is brought to the table, flaming with lighted brandy, the menyn melys is just right for pouring over a portion. Including some of the brandy butter (referred to later) as well, makes a memorable pudding.

Treacle posset

Another of my mother's recipes, this is a traditional drink for cold winter evenings or for someone who has a flu-type cold. Add a teaspoon of black treacle into a cup of hot milk and stir well.

Rice pudding

As long, slow cooking is required, it is better to make this when the oven is being used for something else in order to make the best use of energy. An Aga is ideal. Traditionally, rice pudding was made in an oven which was cooling down after bread and pastries had been cooked. A pressure cooker shortens the cooking time.

114g (4oz) short grain rice
2 tablespoons sugar

1 ltre (1.76 pints)
Pinch of salt

Put the rice, salt and sugar in a heatproof dish and add the milk, stirring well. Cook in a low oven at 150°C (Gas Mark 3) for three hours. Give it a stir every now and again to stop the grains settling in the bottom while it is cooking.

Junket

Junket is the traditional curds and whey that Little Miss Muffet was eating when she was so rudely disturbed by the spider. Junket sachets or tablets are available and normally contain flavourings such as strawberry or banana.

1 pint (568ml) whole milk
2 tablespoons sugar
1 tablet or sachet Junket rennet

Warm the milk to blood heat when it will feel warm to the touch. Add the rennet and sugar and stir well. Leave covered in a warm place, and avoid disturbing it until set. It is best eaten warm, straight away - just in case that spider comes!

Cheese

There are many recipes for cooking with cheese so I have included only those that are particular family favourites.

Welsh rarebit

An old favourite, but it is surprising how many do not know how to make it.

227g (½ lb) cheese
284ml (½ pint) milk
1 tablespoon butter

2 tablespoons plain flour
Pinch of salt
Pinch of black pepper

Melt the butter in a saucepan then mix in the flour until a 'roux' is formed. Add the milk, grated cheese and seasoning. Heat gently, stirring all the time, until the mixture thickens. Serve on buttered toast and season with Worcester sauce.

Cheese fondue

227g (½ lb) cheese
1 garlic clove
1 tablespoon butter

4 tablespoons white wine
4 tablespoons milk
1 tablespoon plain flour

Pinch of salt
Pinch of black pepper

Crush the garlic clove and add to the wine. Leave to stand and meanwhile heat the butter and flour to a roux. Add the cheese, wine, milk and seasonings, and heat slowly, stirring all the time until it thickens.

Welsh cheese pudding

This is an excellent and filling meal. Serve it with sliced tomatoes as a side dish.

227g (8oz) grated cheese 2 eggs
284ml (½ pint) milk Pinch of salt
114g (4 oz) bread crumbs Pinch of black pepper

Separate the eggs and whip the whites until stiff. Meanwhile heat the milk and stir in the breadcrumbs. Remove from the heat and stir in the egg yolks, cheese and seasonings. Leave to cool for ten minutes then fold in the egg whites. Place in a greased, heatproof dish and sprinkle some extra grated cheese on top. Bake in an oven at 200°C (Gas Mark 6) for half an hour, until the top is nicely browned.

Cheesecakes

There are two stages to making cheesecake: the base and then the cheesecake itself. With some recipes there may be a third stage if there is a separate topping.

Biscuit base
One 113g (4oz) packet plain digestive biscuits
56g (2oz) butter

Crush the biscuits with a rolling pin. Melt the butter in a saucepan and add the crumbly mixture. Mix well and press into an oiled cake tin. Leave in the refrigerator until quite cold.

Orange cheesecake

227g (8oz) curd cheese
Half a packet of orange jelly or a sachet of vegetarian carragheen
3 tablespoons water
1 tablespoon sugar
I orange

Add the jelly to water and heat until dissolved. Stir in the sugar and the grated rind and juice of the orange. Beat the cheese until smooth and stir in the orange mixture. Add to the base and leave to set in the refrigerator. Place orange segments on top. (Tinned Mandarin oranges can be used as an alternative).

Blackcurrant cheesecake

The basic recipe above can be used for all sorts of different fruit flavours, depending on the flavour of jelly that is used. If required, a fruit sauce topping can be made and poured over the cheesecake before serving. For example, where a blackcurrant jelly has been used, make a sauce from 4oz of fresh blackcurrants.

Put the blackcurrants in a sieve over a bowl, then mash them with a wooden spoon so that the pulp goes through the sieve, leaving the pips and stalks behind. Add two tablespoons of water and two tablespoons of sugar to the fruit pulp, then heat until the mixture bubbles. Leave until cold then pour over the cheesecake.

Yoghurt

Before yoghurt is used in recipes, it needs to be stabilised, otherwise it will separate leaving small particles. To do this, beat a pint of yoghurt until it is liquid. Take the egg white from one egg and mix this with one tablespoon of cornflour and one tablespoon milk or water. Add to the yoghurt and heat slowly, stirring all the time, until it thickens and resembles thick cream.

Cole slaw

10 tablespoons stabilised yoghurt
1 tablespoon lemon juice or wine vinegar
454g (1lb) shredded white cabbage

1 grated carrot
5 tablespoons mayonnaise
Salt to taste

Shred the cabbage and grate the carrot, then blend in the yoghurt, mayonnaise, lemon juice and salt. Mix thoroughly then refrigerate until ready to use.

Butter

Butter is butter, but it can be presented differently for special occasions.

Herb butter

Finely chopped fresh herbs can be mixed in with butter. It needs to be left for a few hours before use, to give the herb time to permeate the butter. Suitable herbs include parsley, chives or mint.

Brandy butter

Referred to earlier, this is a luxury item to go with the Christmas pudding.

227g (8oz) butter
350g (12oz) icing or caster sugar
6 tablespoons brandy (or rum if preferred)

Cream the butter and gradually work in the sugar and brandy. Refrigerate so that it hardens before use.

Butter icing

This is a nice filling for sponge cakes or to go on top of a special occasion cake. Beat 113g (4oz) butter with 227g (8oz) icing sugar. For a chocolate variation add 4 tablespoons of drinking chocolate or 113g (4oz) finely grated milk chocolate or white chocolate into the mixture.

Buttermilk and whey

Buttermilk and whey are excellent for making scones or for adding to a fruit cake mixture instead of the normal liquid. Buttermilk also mixes well with mashed potato to produce a smooth texture.

Appendix I: Regulations

• Anyone producing milk or dairy products for sale should get hold of all the relevant regulations and advisory publications. It is obviously not possible to list all of them in this book. Contact local DEFRA offices, Environmental Health Departments and the Dairying Inspectorate for further details.

• Join a relevant organisation. For cheesemakers there is the *Specialist Cheesemakers' Association.* They have produced an excellent guide called *The Specialist Cheesemakers' Code of Best Practice.* For ice cream makers there is the *Ice Cream Alliance.* (See Reference section for contact details).

• Milk is recognised in law as coming from cows, goats, sheep and buffaloes.

• Premises producing milk for human consumption must be registered (England and Wales) or licensed (Scotland and Northern Ireland) as a 'production holding'.

• Where milk is processed in any way, the premises must be registered or licensed as a 'dairy establishment'.

• Legislation covers all aspects of milk production, handling and processing, animal health, water supply, raw milk standards, premises and equipment, packaging and labelling, cleaning schedules, whey disposal and keeping records. All dairying establishments must also produce a risk analysis programme that is agreed with their local Environmental Health Department. Once accepted, the producer is allocated a unique number and health mark which is then included on any packaging for traceability purposes within the European Union.

• Those producing dairy products for sale are advised to have full insurance cover.

• Cheesemaking and dairying courses are available at many agricultural colleges, as well as private dairies. Attendance at one of these is highly recommended.

• The following pieces of legislation are relevant:

Dairy Products (Hygiene) Regulations 1995.
Dairy Products (Hygiene) (Amendment) Regulations 1996.
Food Premises (Registration) Regulations 1991.
The Food Safety Act 1990.
Food Safety (General Food Hygiene) Regulations 1995.
The Food Safety (Temperature Control) Regulations 1995.
The Cheese Regulations (Food and Drugs Act).
Weights and Measures Act.
Food Labelling Regulations 1996.
The Ice Cream (Heat Treatment) Regulations.

• The following free publications are available from DEFRA Publications or from the Welsh, Scottish or Northern Ireland Agriculture Departments.

Dairy Products (Hygiene) Regulations 1995. Ref. No: PB2410
The Food Safety Act 1990 and You. PB2507
A Guide to Clean Milk Production. PB0341
A Guide to the Dairy Products (Hygiene) Regulations for Dairy Farmers. PB2338
Short Guide to the Dairy Products (Hygiene) Regulations for Dairy Farmers. PB2339.
A Short Guide to the Dairy Products (Hygiene) Regulations for Farmers Producing and Processing Milk from Goats and Sheep. PB2337

Appendix II: Pressed Cheese Checklist

This is for those who make cheeses regularly, and who are testing acidity at the various stages. It provides general guidelines only, for milk varies according to the dairy animals, the seasons and many other factors.

Caerphilly
Temp. at start: 30°C
Temp. at scald: 34°C
Amt. starter: 1%
Amt. rennet: 15ml/50 litres
Acidity at rennet: 0.20 - 0.23
Acidity at cutting: 0.12 - 0.15
Acidity at draining: 0.17 - 0.19
Acidity at salting: 0.30 - 0.39
Storage temp: 10 - 12°C
Maturing time: 2 weeks

Cheddar
Temp. at start: 30°C
Temp. at scald: 38-40°C
Amt. starter: 1.0 - 1.5%
Amt. rennet: 15ml/50 litres
Acidity at rennet: 0.20 - 0.23
Acidity at cutting: 0.14 - 0.16
Acidity at draining: 0.20 - 0.24
Acidity at salting: 0.65 - 0.85
Storage temp:8 - 11°C
Maturing time: 3 months

Cheshire
Temp. at start: 30°C
Temp. at scald: 34°C
Amt. starter: 1.5 - 2.0%
Amt. rennet: 15ml/50 litres
Acidity at rennet: 0.20 - 0.24
Acidity at cutting: 0.13 - 0.14
Acidity at draining: 0.20 - 0.23
Acidity at salting: 0.55 - 0.85
Storage temp: 8 - 10°C
Maturing time: 1month

Derby
Temp. at start: 29°C
Temp. at scald: 36°C
Amt. starter: 1.5%
Amt. rennet: 15ml/50 litres
Acidity at rennet: 0.18 - 0.19
Acidity at cutting: 0.12
Acidity at draining: 0.15 - 0.19
Acidity at salting: 0.45 - 0.65
Storage temp: 10 - 13°C
Maturing time: 3 months

Double Gloucester
Temp. at start: 29°C
Temp. at scald: 37°C
Amt. starter: 1.5%
Amt. rennet: 13ml/50 litres
Acidity at rennet: 0.19 - 0.20
Acidity at cutting: 0.12 - 0.13
Acidity at draining: 0.19 - 0.23
Acidity at salting: 0.60 - 0.75
Storage temp: 10 - 13°C
Maturing time: 3 months

Dunlop
Temp. at start: 30°C
Temp. at scald: 36°C
Amt. starter: 1.0%
Amt. rennet: 12ml/50 litres
Acidity at rennet: 0.18 - 0.20
Acidity at cutting: 0.12 - 0.13
Acidity at draining: 0.21 - 0.25
Acidity at salting: 0.65 - 0.75
Storage temp: 10 - 15°C
Maturing time: 4 months

Lancashire
Temp. at start: 21°C
Temp. at scald: No scalding
Amt. starter: 0.12%
Amt. rennet: 15ml/50 litres
Acidity at rennet: 0.16 - 0.18
Acidity at cutting: 0.11 - 0.12
Acidity at draining: 0.18 - 0.22
Acidity at salting: 0.9 - 0.99
Storage temp: 12 - 13°C
Maturing time: 2 months

Leicester
Temp. at start: 29°C
Temp. at scald: 36°C
Amt. starter: 0.75%
Amt. rennet: 15ml/50 litres
Acidity at rennet: 0.17 - 0.19
Acidity at cutting: 0.12
Acidity at draining: 0.19 - 0.20
Acidity at salting: 0.45 - 0.65
Storage temp: 9 - 10°C
Maturing time: 3 months

Stilton
Temp. at start: 29°C
Temp. at scald: No scalding
Amt. starter: 0.01%
Amt. rennet: 23ml/50 litres
Acidity at rennet: 0.17 - 0.18
Acidity at cutting: 0.12
Acidity at draining: 0.13 - 0.17
Acidity at salting: 0.55 - 0.65
Storage temp: 7 - 8°C
Maturing time: 3 months

Wensleydale
Temp. at start: 29°C
Temp. at scald: 32°C
Amt. starter: 0.2%
Amt. rennet: 15ml/50 litres
Acidity at rennet: 0.19 - 0.23
Acidity at cutting: 0.14 - 0.15
Acidity at draining: 0.20 -0.24
Acidity at salting: 0.6 - 0.8
Storage temp: 12 - 13°C
Maturing time: 3 weeks

Annatto: 5 - 15ml/50 litres depending on strength of colour required.

Environment:
General conditions - individual cheeses vary in requirements.

Temp. of Dairy: 21-24°C
Drying Area: 18-21°C
Storage Area: 7 -15°C *
Humidity in Storage: 80 - 90% *
Refrigerator: - 4°C
Freezer: - 18°C

* varies according to cheese

Grading cheese

The following grading system is followed during the examination and appraisal of pressed cheeses.

Flavour and aroma	45
Body and texture	40
Colour	5
Outside appearance (finish)	10
Total	*100*

Note: Ripening time after starter - 60 minutes unless stated otherwise in recipe. Maturing times shown are the minimum.

Appendix III: Useful Measurements

Quantities
1 litre = 1000ml = 1.76 pints
1 pint = 568ml
1 gallon = 4.55 litres
1 oz = 28.4g
1 lb = 16 oz = 454g
1 kg = 1000g = 2.2 lb
1 fl.oz = 28.4 ml
1 teaspoon = 5 ml
1 dessertspoon = 10 ml
1 tablespoon = 15 ml

Temperature conversions
Celsius to Fahrenheit:
Multiply by 9
Divide by 5
Add 32

Fahrenheit to Celsius:
Subtract 32
Multiply by 5
Divide by 9

Curd cutting conversions
Half inch: 1.2cm
Inch: 2.5cm
2 inches: 5cm
6 inches: 15cm

Temperatures

Celsius		Fahrenheit
- 18	(Deep freezer)	- 0.4
0	(Freezing point)	32
1		33.8
4	(Refrigerator)	39.2
5		41
10		50
15		59
20		68
25		77
30		86
35		95
40		104
45		113
50		122
55		131
60		140
65		149
66	(30 mins pasteurisation)	150.8
70		158
72	(15 secs pasteurisation)	161.6
75		167
80		176
82	(Quick pasteurisation)	179.6
85		185
90		194
95		203
100	(Boiling point)	212

Pressing Cheese
The pressure of a large commercial cheese press is normally expressed in kN/m^2 or kiloNewtons/square metre where $6.89\ kN/m^2 =$ 1lb force per square inch.

The area referred to is the surface area of the top of the cheese.

The amount of force applied varies directly with the overall weight of the cheese. A cheese with the same surface area but twice the weight of another would require twice the force applied.

A small cheese with 50lb exerted on the top surface area of 21.7sq.in (Wheeler) would experience a force of 2.3lb/sq.in or $16kN/m^2.$

Dry Salting - On average, 2% of weight of curd, eg, 20g per kilo.

Brining - 16% brine = 160ml salt (10.5 level tablespoons) per litre of water.
18% brine = 180ml salt (12 level tablespoons) per litre of water.
20% brine = 200ml salt (13 level tablespoons) per litre of water.

% starter	Amount of starter in relation to quantity of milk			
	12.5 litres	*25 litres*	*50 litres*	*100 litres of milk*
0.1	12.5 ml	25ml	50ml	l00ml
0.2	25	50	100	200
0.3	37.5	75	150	300
0.4	50	100	200	400
0.5	62.5	125	250	500
0.6	75	150	300	600
0.7	87.5	175	350	700
0.8	100	200	400	800
0.9	112.5	225	450	900
1.0	125	250	500	1000 (1 litre)

Glossary

Acidity - percentage of lactic acid present in milk, curd or whey.

Acidmeter - device for measuring acidity

Ammoniated - condition where ammonia gas is given off by over-ripe cheese

Annatto - natural colouring agent from *Bixa orellana* plant used to colour cheese or butter

Aroma - relative smell of different cheeses

Bacteriophage - virus that can affect starters by reproducing in and then killing off the bacteria

Bandaging - binding of maturing hard cheeses

Bloomy rind - light white down that develops on surface of some cheeses, eg, Camembert

Body - applies to cheese, eg, whether flaky or hard

Brining - immersing cheeses in salt solution

Casein - the main protein in milk which is coagulated when rennet is added to milk

Cheddaring - where cheese curd is cut into blocks for a specific time to develop acidity and texture

Cheesecloth - close textured material for draining curds and bandaging pressed cheeses

Coagulation - curdling of milk into curds and whey

Culture - strain of lactic acid producing bacteria

Curd - the solid product of coagulation of milk

Dairy establishment - legally recognised premises where milk is processed

DVI - direct vat inoculation starter which does not need to be incubated before use

Follower - block on cheese mould on which press exerts pressure

Grading - system of checking finished cheeses

Homogenised - where fat is broken into small pieces and distributed throughout milk

Hot Iron Test - old way of testing acidity by putting curd to heat and checking length of curd string

Humidity - percentage of moisture in the air

Lactose - milk sugar

Maturing - process of aging and ripening of pressed cheeses

Mesophilic - starter cultures that are incubated in a temperature range of 20 - 35°C

Mother culture - starter culture of lactic acid producing bacteria from which further sub-cultures can be made

Milling - process of breaking up curd into pieces

Moulds - Containers for shaping or holding curd for draining or pressing. Also refers to white bloom and blue-veined moulds that are required in some cheeses, eg, Camembert, Gorgonzola

Pasteurisation - heat treatment of milk to kill or reduce pathogens

Pathogens - bacteria that can cause illness

Phenolphthalein - colour reagent used in the testing of acidity

Pitching - allowing the previously stirred curds to settle in the whey during cheesemaking

Pressing - process of applying gradual pressure to cheese in order to remove whey and consolidate texture

Production holding - legally recognised premises where milk is produced

Raw milk - milk that has not been heat treated above 40°C

Rennet - substance used to curdle milk

Rind - outer, drier surface of cheese

Ripening - of milk: allowing lactic acid to develop before adding rennet.
　　　　- of soft cheeses: as they develop in storage

Running - process of draining whey from curds

Salting - the adding of dry salt to cheese curds

Scalding - heating or cooking the curd during the process of making a cheese

Semi-skimmed milk - heat treated milk with a fat content between 1.5 - 1.8%

Skimmed milk - milk that has been heat-treated and has a maximum fat content of 0.5%

Sodium hydroxide - solution of caustic soda in water, with chemical formula of NaOH, used in the testing of lactic acid levels

Starter - lactic acid producing culture of bacteria

Sterilisation - heat treatment to kill pathogens

Sub-culturing - using original mother culture to produce more starter

Sweating - fat oozing from stored cheeses

Taint - a smell or taste transmitted to milk

Texture - depending on moisture content the texture of a cheese may be open, close, firm, etc.

Thermophilic - starter cultures that are incubated at higher temperatures, usually in the range of 35 - 60°C

Top-stirring - stirring the surface in order to mix in any cream that may be collecting

Trier - utensil for taking a sample plug of cheese

Vat - water-jacketed container for making cheese

Washed rind - cheeses that are regularly washed, eg, in brine or beer, etc, as they mature in storage

Whey - the liquid part of milk left after the curds have been removed

Reference section

Bibliography
Cheesmaking Practice. R. Scott. Elsevier Publishers.
Dairy Microbiology. The National Dairy Council.
Starter Cultures for Farmhouse Dairy Products. ADAS.

Organisations
British Cheese Board. Tel: 0117 921 1744 www.cheeseboard.co.uk
DEFRA Food Hygiene Division. Tel: 020 7238 6368
Dept. of Health Food Hygiene Legislation Policy Unit. Tel: 020 7972 5078.
The Specialist Cheesemakers' Association. Tel: 020 7253 2114.
www.specialistcheesemakers.co.uk
The Ice Cream Alliance. Tel: 01332 203333. www.ice-cream.org
Cheesemakers' Association of Wales (CAWS). www.cheesewales.com
British Sheep Dairying Association. www.sheepdairying.com

Suppliers
Armfield Ltd. (Small scale cheese vats and equipment). Tel: 01425 478781 (Hants).
www.armfield.co.uk
Ascott Smallholding Supplies Ltd. (Small scale dairying equipment and supplies).
Tel: 0845 130 6285 (Shropshire). www.ascott.biz
Carlisle Process Systems Ltd. (Farm scale cheese equipment). Tel: 01935 818800
(Dorset). www.carlisleuk.com
C. Van't Riet. (Vats and cheesemaking equipment). Tel: 31 01725 71304 (Netherlands).
Chr. Hansen (UK) Ltd. (Starter cultures). Tel: 01488 689800 (Berks) www.chr-hansen.com
Danisco (UK) Ltd. (Starter cultures). Tel: 01933 304200 (Northants). www.danisco.com
Danro Ltd. (Labels and labelling equipment). Tel: 01455 847061/2 (Leicester).
www.danroltd.co.uk
Fullwood. (Milking equipment). Tel: 01691 622391.
Goat Nutrition Ltd. (Small scale dairying and packaging equipment and supplies).
Tel: 01233 770780 (Kent). www.gnltd.co.uk
Moorlands Cheesemakers. (Small scale cheesemaking equipment and wide range of
cultures). Tel: 01749 850108 (Somerset). www.cheesemaking.co.uk
Oxmoor Smallholder Supplies. (Small scale dairying and cheese equipment and supplies).
Tel: 01757 288186 (East Yorkshire).
R & J Wheeler (Engineers) (Cheese presses and equipment). Tel: 01932 832238 (Devon).
Rosslab plc. (Acidmeters). Tel: 01625 610077 (Cheshire).
Stratton Sales Ltd. (Cheesemaking supplies). Tel: 01749 344071 (Somerset).
www.strattonsales.co.uk

Courses
Agrifood Centre, University of Plymouth. Tel: 01626 325858 (Devon).
Brackenhurst Hall. Tel: 01636 817000 (Notts)
Mike Staff. Tel: 01278 732563 (Somerset).
Otley College. Tel: 01473 785543 (Suffolk).
Reaseheath College. Tel: 01270 625131 (Cheshire).
The Cheddar Gorge Company. Tel: 01934 742810 (Somerset).
West Highland Dairy. Tel: 0159 957 7203 (Ross-Shire).

Dairies open to visitors
Cricketer Farm (Somerset). Tel: 01278 732084. www.cricketerfarm.co.uk (Pre-book)
Monkland Cheese Dairy. (Hereford). Tel: 01568 720307. www.mousetrapcheese.co.uk
The Cheddar Gorge Co. (Somerset). Tel: 01934 742810.
Wensleydale Visitor Centre. (North Yorks). Tel: 01969 667664. www.wensleydale.co.uk

Index

103